THE CONSTELLATION QUESTION

SMITHSONIAN STUDIES IN HISTORY AND TECHNOLOGY

NUMBER 5

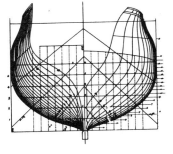

The Constellation Question

PART 1

The Story of the *Constellation* ∽ *Howard I. Chapelle*

PART 2

Comments on "The Story of the *Constellation* ∽ *Leon D. Polland*

PART 3

An Outline of the Present Restoration ∽ *Leon D. Polland*

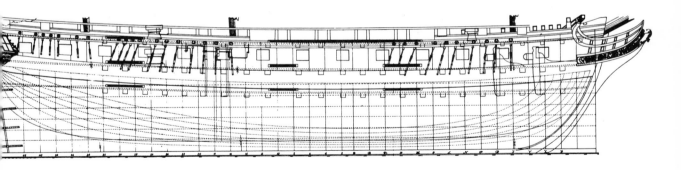

SMITHSONIAN INSTITUTION PRESS

City of Washington • 1970

SERIAL PUBLICATIONS OF THE SMITHSONIAN INSTITUTION

The emphasis upon publications as a means of diffusing knowledge was expressed by the first Secretary of the Smithsonian Institution. In his formal plan for the Institution, Joseph Henry articulated a program that included the following statement: "It is proposed to publish a series of reports, giving an account of the new discoveries in science, and of the changes made from year to year in all branches of knowledge not strictly professional." This keynote of basic research has been adhered to over the years in the issuance of thousands of titles in serial publications under the Smithsonian imprint, commencing with *Smithsonian Contributions to Knowledge* in 1848 and continuing with the following active series:

Smithsonian Annals of Flight
Smithsonian Contributions to Anthropology
Smithsonian Contributions to Astrophysics
Smithsonian Contributions to Botany
Smithsonian Contributions to the Earth Sciences
Smithsonian Contributions to Paleobiology
Smithsonian Contributions to Zoology
Smithsonian Studies in History and Technology

In these series, the Institution publishes original articles and monographs dealing with the research and collection of its several museums and offices and of professional colleagues at other institutions of learning. These papers report newly acquired facts, synoptic interpretations of data, or original theory in specialized fields. Each publication is distributed by mailing lists to libraries, laboratories, institutes, and interested specialists throughout the world. Individual copies may be obtained from the Smithsonian Institution Press as long as stocks are available.

S. Dillon Ripley
Secretary
Smithsonian Institution

For sale by the Superintendent of Documents, U.S. Government Printing Office
Washington, D.C. 20402 - Price $3.75

Foreword

This unusual volume has an unusual history. It began as a monograph by Mr. Howard I. Chapelle—essentially the present Part 1—and as a paper by Mr. Leon D. Polland—presented before sections of the Society of Naval Architects and Marine Engineers on 7 May 1966—which forms the basis for the rebuttal contained in Parts 2 and 3. Mr. Chapelle's manuscript was accepted for publication by the Smithsonian Institution Press in the spring of 1968. In this manuscript Mr. Chapelle, who is as straightforward as he is learned, set forth his reasons for questioning the authenticity of the present day *Constellation*. When, in July 1968, a Baltimore newspaper announced the forthcoming publication under the headline "Constellation Now Under Fire From Smithsonian Historian," the Institution began to hear from those who disagreed with Mr. Chapelle. Some of our correspondents, misunderstanding the nature of the Smithsonian, argued that publication of Mr. Chapelle's manuscript by the Smithsonian Institution Press would constitute official government sponsorship of the author's conclusions. Many urged us to abandon the whole project on the grounds that publication would constitute a kind of desecration of a precious national shrine.

Faced with these suggestions, which occasionally seemed almost to be demands, the Institution found itself in somewhat of a dilemma. Since the Smithsonian Institution Press has always been a publisher of scholarly manuscripts, more akin to a university press than to a government publication office, its standards and procedures are those appropriate to any scholarly publisher. Given Mr. Chapelle's towering reputation in his field, and given the enthusiastic reports of the outside scholars to whom his manuscript was referred, the Press felt an obligation to stick by its original decision. In reaffirming our determination to proceed with Mr. Chapelle's manuscript, we stated that: "In publishing it, the Institution certainly does not presume to guarantee the correctness of everything in the manuscript. The Institution does, however, believe that the manuscript represents a serious contribution to scholarship, that it deserves to be made available to interested scholars and laymen, and that its reception by other competent authorities in the field over the years will be the best test of its validity."

On the other hand, we recognized that the debate between Mr. Chapelle and Mr. Polland—highly technical though it may be—was not quite the same as a dispute between scholars about, say, the interpretation of a Babylonian text. Various agencies of the federal government and of the State of Maryland had been involved in the restoration of the ship; numerous private citizens had contributed their time and money to the restoration; and the ship herself had indeed become a national historic landmark. In view of all this, it seemed to us that the mere publication of Mr. Chapelle's controversial manuscript might not adequately discharge the Institution's obligation.

v

It was in this context that we began discussions with the *Constellation* Restoration Committee, and particularly with its Chairman, Mr. Gordon M. F. Stick. To our great delight, we learned that the Committee shared our concern for the freedom of scholarly expression and was not unalterably opposed to the publication of Mr. Chapelle's manuscript. Rather, the Committee urged that it be given an opportunity to review the manuscript and to provide a rebuttal for publication along with it. Mr. Polland, Technical Advisor and Chief of Construction and Repair for the *Constellation* Project, was chosen to prepare the rebuttal. With Mr. Chapelle's gracious consent to the delay this necessarily involved, and with the Committee's agreement that his manuscript would be subjected to the same rigorous standards that are applied to all Smithsonian Institution Press publications, the present volume was born.

If I may be permitted a personal observation, I would say that as a layman I find the question of whether today's *Constellation* is the original *Constellation* by no means the only interesting part of this book. I recall the laconic words of Captain Joshua Slocum (or his ghostwriter) as he described the rebuilding of the extraordinary sloop *Spray* in *Sailing Alone Around the World:* "Now, it is a law in Lloyd's that the *Jane* repaired all out of the old until she is entirely new is still the *Jane*. The *Spray* changed her being so gradually that it was hard to say at what point the old died or new took birth, and was no matter." As a layman, I find this book fascinating in a number of respects quite different from the question which it sets out to discuss. It is a privilege and a pleasure to watch two scholars as erudite as Mr. Chapelle and Mr. Polland set out to prove their respective sides of so complex a controversy. In the process, one learns an enormous amount about shipbuilding techniques, about naval architecture, and even about government procurement procedures through the centuries. It is conceivable that some readers may finish the book and still be unable to answer *The Constellation Question*. But I venture to say that they will agree with me that their time has been well spent.

Charles Blitzer
Assistant Secretary
for History and Art
Smithsonian Institution

February 1970

Contents

ᴄᴧꙩ

PART 3—An Outline of the Present Restoration, by Leon D. Polland

PART 1

The Story of the *Constellation*

Introduction

DURING THE LAST HALF CENTURY a number of old ships have been repaired, reconstructed, or restored to preserve them as historical and educational objects of local or national interest. The historical, or technical, accuracy in the details of a few of these ships has been sharply questioned by some maritime historians and marine archeologists having knowledge of sailing ship design, construction, and rigging. This has been the case with the reconstruction of the frigate *Constitution*, in which hull details, fittings, armament, and rig have features of various periods that did not coexist. Yet they were incorporated in the reconstruction, with the result that the reconstructed ship does not represent her at any one period of her career.

In the case of the *Constellation*, whose reconstruction or restoration is now the subject of debate, the question is a basic one of identity: is the existing ship the original frigate, lengthened amidships and retopped as a corvette, or is she a vessel of entirely new design and construction built in 1853?

One of six frigates—three 44-gun ships and three 36-gun ships—authorized by Congress on 27 March 1794, the *Constellation* was built between 1794 and 1797, at Baltimore, Maryland, in a leased shipyard. She saw action during the quasi-war with France, 1798–99, and was blockaded at Norfolk during the whole of the War of 1812. She was one of three United States naval vessels that engaged a large Algerine frigate soon after that war and was never in action again.

After the War of 1812 she received many repairs and was employed until 1853, when she was "administratively rebuilt" as a spar-decked corvette having different dimensions than the original frigate. She was then employed on foreign stations "to show the flag" and as a training ship. The vessel received numerous and, in the 1870s, rather extensive repairs. Finally, she was permanently stationed at the Naval Training Station, Newport, Rhode Island. Becoming unserviceable, she was moved to Boston and was the subject of discussion as to whether or not she should be restored by the Navy.

At the end of World War II, a group of Baltimoreans applied to the Navy for the possession of the vessel for restoration, and the ship was delivered to them at Baltimore

Howard I. Chapelle is Senior Historian, Department of Industry, National Museum of History and Technology, Smithsonian Institution.

in 1953. It was then generally believed that the ship was the old Baltimore-built frigate altered to a sloop-of-war or a corvette.

When the plan to bring the *Constellation* to Baltimore was first publicized in 1946, I thought that attention should be given to extensive documentation and to technical evidence that showed the ship could not be the old frigate lengthened and retopped as a corvette but was rather a replacement for her, built entirely new, on a new design, at Norfolk in 1853–55. This was discussed in a rather lengthy correspondence in the *Baltimore Sun* in 1946–47, in which I identified the technical evidence and gave references to much of the documentation just mentioned.

A committee of Baltimore citizens had been formed to manage the reconstruction and to do the necessary research for restoring the existing corvette as the Baltimore-built frigate. These gentlemen have attempted to refute the evidence I supplied. The resulting debate has continued intermittently until the present time.

The *Constellation* Committee presented its claims, based chiefly on a brief or memorandum prepared by Franklin Delano Roosevelt in 1918, with their documentation added, in a historical society's magazine in 1961.[1] Another presentation was made in a paper read before a meeting of an American professional society's sections in 1966,[2] supplementing the 1961 publication.

These two documents contain the claims of the Baltimore proponents, detailed at length, and allow an analysis of those claims to be made.

Acknowledgment is made of the generous aid given the author by Dr. Philip K. Lundeberg, Curator in Charge, Naval History, Department of Armed Services History, National Museum of History and Technology, Smithsonian Institution, and H. Crane Miller, Assistant General Counsel, Smithsonian Institution.

Historical Notes

THERE ARE PRELIMINARIES to this examination that require attention. One is the sequence of discussion to be followed. It is not entirely chronological, owing to the requirements imposed by the Baltimore Committee's arguments, which maintain that the present *Constellation* is the frigate cut down to a corvette and lengthened in 1853–55. This has led the Committee to the necessity of proving that the old frigate of 1794–97 was not built from the official plans and design but rather from plans of a design made by the owner of the yard in which the frigate was built, David Stodder, in order to account for the contrary evidence of hull form and dimensions. Hence it becomes necessary to examine the history of the design and construction of the frigate and then to make a similar examination of the design and building of the corvette of 1853–55. This will lead to nonchronological references or documentation as the arguments are developed.

Taking the chronological history of the building of the 1794–97 frigate at Baltimore [3] as the starting point will do much to bring some order into the examination. As early as 1791 a Congressional committee had been investigating the possible establishment of a naval force to protect the American merchant marine. The committee dealt with the "War Office" of the executive branch, as there was then no admiralty or naval office. The War Office, later called Department of War, had as its cabinet member, or Secretary, General Henry Knox, in whose hands President Washington had placed the responsibilities of meeting with the Congressional committee and the eventual implementation of any Congressional act on the subject.

General Knox had no professional knowledge of naval affairs or of shipbuilding. Therefore, very early in the investigation, he sought competent advice. Since Congress would demand full descriptions of the ships and estimates of cost when considering an authorization for the construction of a naval force, he obtained the assistance of two competent Philadelphia shipbuilders: John Wharton, who had designed war vessels for the Pennsylvania state navy and may also have designed some of the Continental Navy frigates, as well as a design for three proposed 74-gun ships; and William Penrose, a member of a then prominent Philadelphia shipbuilding family who had long experience in the profession. Knox also obtained the assistance of John Barry and other experienced shipmasters, most of them veterans of the Revolution. Among these were men who knew the frigate *South Carolina,* a vessel designed in France, built in Holland, and loaned to the state of South Carolina. [4] Though her service dur-

5

FIGURE 1.—Model of frigate *Constellation* built on the 1794 official draught and offsets. Now in the Hall of the Armed Services History, National Museum of History and Technology, Smithsonian Institution.

ing the Revolution in the South Carolina state navy was very short, she made a great impression because of her unusual length and very heavy armament; she apparently became the inspiration for the exceptionally large men-of-war contemplated by Knox and his consultants.

Since the naval force was to be employed primarily against the Barbary pirates, whose largest ships were of 44 guns, the vessels considered for the American naval force ranged from 24- to 44-gun frigates. It was decided early in the investigation that these vessels were to be an overmatch for any of their class, or rate, in any navy; the 44s were to be able to fight anything of less than 64 guns.

By 1793 the desired dimensions of the ships had been established. Late in that year, Knox obtained the services of Joshua Humphreys, another Philadelphia builder, who had been a partner of Wharton in the construction of the Continental Navy frigate *Randolph* and who was also Wharton's nephew. Humphreys was to prepare the final estimates without pay, but probably with hope of future employment if the vessels were authorized.

On 27 March 1794 the Congress passed the act authorizing the construction and fitting out of six frigates—three 44s and three 36s—and the War Office began to set up the necessary organizations to construct the ships. On 28 June 1794 Joshua Humphreys was appointed to design the frigates. His wages began 1 May 1794, however, to compensate him for his work on the estimates and other services. The estimates had been completed sometime earlier than 27 March 1794.

Humphreys prepared a model, and probably a draught, to show his concept of the 44-gun design, conforming to the general dimensions established by the earlier consultations between Knox and his advisers. This model was submitted to Knox but no immediate decision was made. On 21 June 1794, however, Humphreys had been ordered to erect a large, temporary mould-loft in his yard. Fortunately, a large loft was found in Philadelphia and, to save time, this was rented on Humphreys' assurances that it could be made to serve the purpose. It had been decided that the lofting for each of the two classes of frigates should be done in this loft and the moulds, or patterns, be made there and shipped to the building yard of each of the ships. This would speed up the preliminaries to beginning erection and construction and also insure that the ships of a class would be alike in lines. The moulds for the shaping of frame timbers were to be accompanied by rough moulds; sets of these for the two classes of frigates were to be set aside for use in cutting timber in the forests. Each yard was to receive a draught and other necessary information.

It is now necessary to introduce Josiah Fox, a thirty-year-old English master shipbuilder. This man had been trained in the Royal Navy dockyard at Portsmouth, completing his apprenticeship on 9 October 1786. He had then worked in English shipyards and later traveled in Europe studying shipbuilding and shipbuilding timber. He came to America in the fall of 1793, pursuing his studies during what was intended to be a short visit. Upon his arrival he visited a cousin, Andrew Ellicott, a prominent American land surveyor. Impressed by Fox, Ellicott took him to meet Captain John Barry, who was also impressed by the young Englishman. As a result Fox was introduced to Knox and interrogated by both Barry and Knox. This led to an offer of employment in the design of the frigates. While the appointment was pending, Fox volunteered to make a proposal draught, which he did and submitted to Knox in the spring of 1794. As the authorization did not permit use of two designers, Fox was made a "clerk" in the War Office, temporarily, to allow his employment as Humphreys' assistant in the preparation of the designs and in the lofting, mould-making, etc., for which it was soon obvious that Fox was better trained than Humphreys, who had never served a full apprenticeship—the builder to whom he had been apprenticed died before Humphreys had completed his time.

Knox and his advisers did not accept the preliminary designs—Humphreys' model and Fox's draught—giving instead, specific instructions for preparation of the final designs. These appear, from the available information, to have included elements of both preliminary designs, to some extent at least.

Another shipwright was obtained as draughtsman and loftsman: William Doughty, who had been employed by Humphreys. The designs were first prepared, offset measurements were then scaled from the drawings and lofted full size, then moulds were made. Copies of the design draughts were also made to accompany the moulds, as well as inboard plans, specifications or building instructions, and some sketches and special instructions required to guide the building mastershipwrights. Most if not all of this work seems to have been supervised by Fox. He and Humphreys were then on friendly terms.

It had been decided by Knox and his consultants that the framing of all the frigates was to be live oak, which could be obtained only on the coasts of South Carolina and Georgia. Hence it was going to be necessary to send men and rough moulds there to get out the "crooked timbers," or "crooks" that would be required for each ship, and trim these to "flitch" (rough timber or plank dressed on opposite two sides, bark on remaining two sides).

As it turned out, the live oak was the cause of much delay in construction. The large timbers required made it necessary to work over a considerable area, creating transportation difficulties. Furthermore, the timber had to be cut in winter, when the sap was down. The winter of 1794–95 was a wet and stormy one in Georgia. Though a good part of the summer of 1794 had been spent in preparation, the living and working conditions of the loggers worsened as winter approached and there was much sickness. Many of the woodcutters left as a result. Vessels, mostly lumber schooners, made one round trip, but weather and sickness prevented some of them from making a second voyage. A load of timber for the New York frigate was lost off Hatteras, and one load was in a vessel blown off shore, ending at Nantucket instead of New York. The shipping of timber north became the cause of serious delays in the late stages of construction of the frigates and eventually led to extensive substitution of local white oak for the specified live oak. All timber was cut by government contract.[5]

In spite of careful planning, timber procurement was never satisfactory and the superintendents had to spend much time in efforts to obtain lumber so that progress could be maintained in the construction of the frigates. At times this difficulty became acute and brought work to a halt. Such delays eventually led to the temporary cancellation of the frigates intended to be built at New York and Norfolk, since little progress had been made on them when peace with Algiers was obtained.

To return to the chronological history of the building of the frigates, on 1 April 1794 the Secretary of the Treasury was notified that President Washington had named the port cities in which the ships were to be built. One 36-gun frigate was assigned to Baltimore. Early in June 1794 Thomas Truxtun was appointed a captain in the naval force. He was ordered, shortly afterward, to Baltimore as superintendent of construction.

Investigation had shown it to be impractical to build the frigates by contract so leased shipyards were to be used. Truxtun was ordered to find a suitable yard and a master shipwright, or "constructor." This title was used instead of master shipwright in correspondence, resulting in a misunderstanding—these "constructors" were yard operators, in the modern sense of yard foremen or managers, not in the sense of naval architects.

Truxtun finally selected the shipyard of David Stodder on Harris Creek. This was a large yard with some useful buildings for storage, a passable entry road, and room for the then unusually long building ways that would be required. Little is known about Stodder; there is only evidence of his having built some merchant ships of 200 to 600 tons and a number of schooners and brigs. Undoubtedly he was a reputable and reasonably competent merchant vessel builder, since Truxtun arranged his employment. (At Boston the Hartt yard was leased, but the owner of this yard was not the "constructor," and this was apparently the case at the New York and Gosport [Norfolk] yards.) After making this decision Truxtun reported to the War Office at Philadelphia and apparently discussed the Baltimore arrangements with Knox.

Upon returning to Baltimore, Truxtun supervised the construction of the building ways, requiring the use of piles, cribbing, and fill, which occupied both Stodder and Truxtun until timber arrived. Mr. Morgan, who was to have been the constructor of the Norfolk frigate, had been detached and sent to Georgia in the Summer of 1794 to prepare for cutting the live oak, which began in the fall under great difficulties. Truxton's correspondence shows the universal concern in the yards regarding timber supply.

When the live-oak flitch began to arrive in the yards in the early spring of 1795, it was found that many of the large timbers, when dressed, or shaped, to the moulds and bevels, showed rot pockets or "black heart," making the sticks worthless for their purpose. As a result, time and labor were lost and replacement timber came in slowly, though sometimes enough sound timber could be obtained for conversion to another use. These difficulties finally made it necessary for Humphreys and others to be sent to the Chesapeake and to the Catskills to obtain white oak as a substitute for some of the live oak.

Meanwhile, the inboard plans of the frigates were being drawn under Fox's supervision, from September 1794 to the spring of 1795; these showed construction and layout of the interior of the ships. No copies of these have been found but such plans are mentioned in correspondence.

The moulds for the Baltimore frigate arrived at the yard sometime in the late fall of 1794. On 14 May 1795 Truxtun reported that the Baltimore yard had the keel and keelson timbers and that most of the live oak in hand had been shaped to the moulds and bevels. No date has been found for the laying of the keel, but Secretary Pickering reported on 12 December 1795 that the keel was laid and bolted together, two thirds of the live oak was in hand, part of the frames had been assembled, and much of the planking was in the yard.[6] In November 1796 the Secretary of War wrote to Stodder to speed up construction as his ship was behind the larger frigates at Philadelphia and Boston in state of completion.

Progress in January 1797, as reported by the Secretary of War, showed the Baltimore frigate to have had all of her frames erected, much of the planking (wales and black strakes) in place—the bottom then being planked—ceiling, clamps, and other longitudinal timbers in place, with launching expected in May. Deck beams, knees and hardware, rigging, blocks, etc., were then in the yard.[7] On 17 April 1797 the Secretary again wrote Stodder about delay. On 16 June the Secretary reported that the Baltimore frigate had her bottom joinered and caulked, the lower deck laid, the others well advanced, head, quarter galleries, and stern partly done, bowsprit almost ready to put on board, etc.

There was concern about launching these large ships when this became imminent. The Philadelphia frigate had been launched 10 May 1797 and had gone off the launching ways too early and too fast and had suffered some damage. (When the

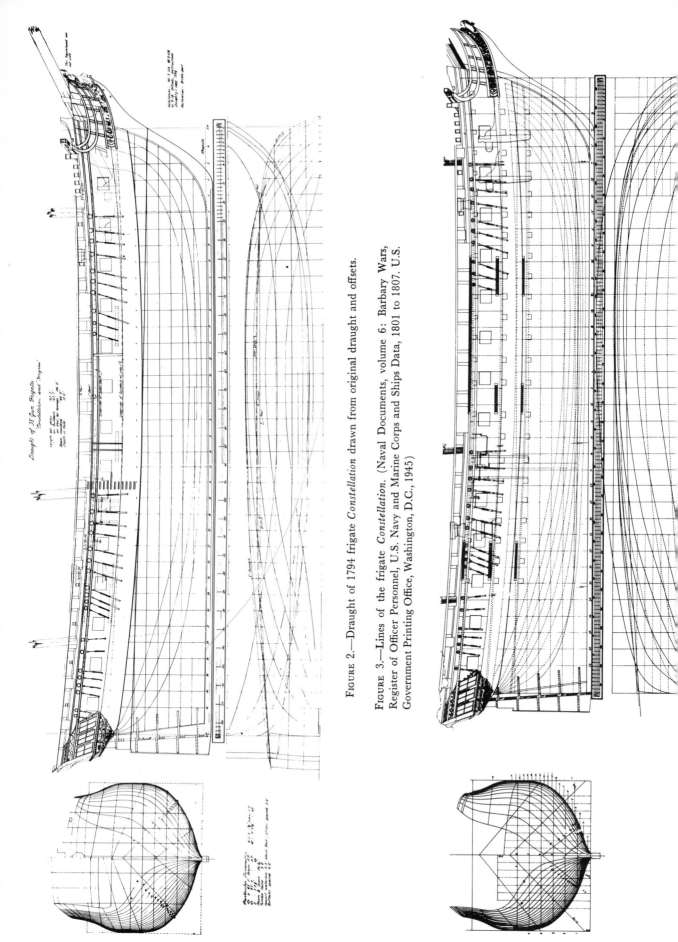

FIGURE 2.—Draught of 1794 frigate *Constellation* drawn from original draught and offsets.

FIGURE 3.—Lines of the frigate *Constellation*. (Naval Documents, volume 6: Barbary Wars, Register of Officer Personnel, U.S. Navy and Marine Corps and Ships Data, 1801 to 1807. U.S. Government Printing Office, Washington, D.C., 1945)

Boston ship was launched on 21 October she stuck on the ways, but was finally launched without damage to the hull.) As a result Humphreys was sent to Baltimore to help Stodder, and the *Constellation* was launched 7 September 1797.

In the chronological account of building the *Constellation,* mention has been made of the draught and offsets. In the period the *Constellation* was built it had long been customary to build from plans, not from half models. In the case of the *Randolph* only the building plan survives, as does also another Revolutionary War period plan for the 74-gun ships that were never built.[8] However, decorative half models were occasionally built—Joshua Humphreys had built such a half model of the proposed Continental Navy 74s (now in Independence Hall, Philadelphia) which follows the lines shown in the plan, or draught, but also shows departures in details. He also built a model of his proposed 44-gun frigate design and presented it to Knox, as stated earlier. This type of model was too fragile for use in the loft or in construction but did serve to show the shape of a hull to laymen better than would a plan.

The draughts for the *Constitution* and *Constellation* classes were on a nonstandard (about $5/16'' = 1'$ graphic-scale, drawn in india ink on handmade drawing paper. The plans C&R 40–7–11A and C&R 40–7–11B showed the sheer elevation, or broadside view, with the location of every other frame; room and space was 26 inches. Horizontal or water lines spaced three feet apart are also shown, as are all details of cutwaters, head rails, and quarter galleries, with location of all gunports. The various mouldings or sheer lines are shown, along with rudder and sternpost rake and stem rake. On this plan the location of capstans, hatches, pumps, bitts ,and deck heights are also shown in profile and location of masts is established; a copy, C&R 41–9–1P, does not show deck detail. Buttock-bow lines, shown as curves in dotted lines, on the profile of the hull, represent longitudinal sections through the hull parallel to the centerline, and are spaced two feet apart. This view of the hull design determines the appearance of the ship, and in the buttock-bow curves, something of the form of the hull.

Hull form, however, is developed to the greater extent in the body plan, which shows cross sections through one side of the hull, at right angles to the centerline. Since the hull will be alike on both sides, that is all that need be considered in either draught or half-model. This plan for the 36-gun frigates showed the shape of every other frame, at the stations shown in the sheer elevation. Here the waterlines are horizontal and straight; the vertical section lines, that is, the "buttock-bow" lines, are straight.

The half-breadth plan is what the name indicates; it shows the shape of the sheer and waterlines in plan view, with frame stations as straight lines at right angles to the centerline, and the buttock-bow lines are straight and parallel to the centerline. This is the final projection to show hull form. The lines were drawn to inside of planking at this period, "moulded," so that offsets produced moulds to the shape of the frames.

Diagonals—straight lines at various angles to the centerline in the body plan— are fairing or proving lines and are generally shown as long curves superimposed on the half-breadth plan. Carving is indicated on the sheer elevation but, in a class of ships on one design, the carving shown would not be employed but would be only to indicate the quantity to be used, or just to decorate the drawing.

A drawing of this kind required much time to complete. The first or master drawing would probably require 40 to 100 working man-hours, depending upon the time needed to establish the design and how rapidly the draughtsman was able to fair and prove the many projections required.

It is probable, in the case of these frigates, that offsets were taken immediately when the master draught was completed, using dividers and the graphic scale.

Offsets are measurements scaled from the draught in feet, inches, and eighths, by which the lines of the ship were drawn full size on the mould-loft floor. For the original draught for the *Constellation* frigate-class there are about 1180 entries in the offset table.[9] After the lines were laid down in the loft and given final fairing, the individual measurements on the loft floor, that had been corrected in fairing, were entered into the offset table to give a final and correct record for future reference. The scaling of draught measurements would be a 20- to 30-man-hour job, laying down and final fairing might have taken 300–350 man-hours, employing trained loftsmen. (The *Constellation*'s original offsets are now represented in the Fox papers at Salem, Massachusetts, by a museum transcript, the original having been extracted unlawfully by a recent visitor.)

Moulds were next made for every piece of timber to go into the stem, stern, keel, and keelson structures and for each of the frames; the latter were formed of a number of "crooks" or futtocks, that were required to form a complete frame rail to rail. Since each half-frame would require 10 to 12 pieces, the moulds were numerous. Approximately 200 to 250 moulds would be required, excluding about 40 rough moulds for each ship, which would be the first gotten out for cutting timber. Moulds were of thin plank, suitably identified, and were accompanied by bevel boards for all frame timbers.

In the case of these frigates, additional plans were required, such as "inboard works" and deck arrangements, previously mentioned, as well as sketches. Specifications or "building instructions" also had to be written. Next, copies of each had to be made for the three frigates of each of the two classes, and Fox and Doughty were under some pressure to get these copies to the yards.

Tracing was not then possible, so the plans were sometimes pricked through the master plan into the copy with a needle, producing very small holes in the copy which were used to guide the draughtsman in drawing the duplicate. An 1827 statement by Fox, however, shows that after he lifted the offsets from the two master plans, he used these to lay out the necessary duplicate plans; a much faster and more precise method. Since none of the surviving frigate plans shows pricking, there can be no doubt that the copies were drawn by use of offsets.

It seems quite evident that both Doughty and Fox made the duplicate plans of each class of frigate; between the two men they must have drawn six copies for the yards and two for the War Office files, and also Fox and Humphreys retained copies, altogether ten plans, two of which may have been the master draughts. All except the last were drawn from corrected offsets; the master draughts were the original design plans and would probably be the one of each frigate-class retained by Fox. The conversion of a design from draught to mould-loft to ship required much time and labor, it can be seen.

In view of the fact timber was worked with manual tools—axe, adze, "frame" or pit saws, and cross-handled augers—production per man-hour in the shipyards was relatively small. Hence large gangs of carpenters were employed and the working day was from sunrise to sunset. With good management, some builders in this period could "run up" a ship in a matter of a few months under such conditions. But this was not the case with the frigates being built in the 1794 program. Though the preliminary stages in construction of the *Constellation* had proceeded rapidly, lack of timber and labor difficulties prevented any schedule for completion being maintained and, like *Congress* at Portsmouth, New Hampshire, and the *United States* at Philadelphia, *Constellation* was late in launching.

One of the problems faced in the design of these frigates, inherent in their very size, was longitudinal strength. The French, who had built large men-of-war, had met with this problem as early as 1746 when they tried diagonal planking inside of the frames and, again, in 1772 the frigate *L'Oiseau* was built with the outboard planking diagonal. The Americans, in 1794, resorted to the use of "dagger knees" at deck beams, secured inside the ceiling, or inboard planking. These knees stood at about 45 degrees to the vertical with lower ends butted together. Thus, the lower arms of each knee crossed, and were fastened to, three or more frames; the upper arms rested alongside and against deck beams. The chief objections to this system were the weight of structure it entailed and the space occupied, which reduced stowage. It was also found that longitudinal strength, by this system, was not improved as much as expected. The use of additional longitudinal timbers inside the hull and backing frames, which had been employed since 1600, met with the same objections. The 1794–98 frigates all showed longitudinal weakness, and hogged within ten years after launching; the surviving ships were badly hogged by 1835.

In planning the construction of the frigates, Knox had set up an organizational plan for control of costs and for supervision of construction.[10] The plan of operation called for an Agent to be appointed to each yard, who was to hire labor, purchase materials and equipment, rigging, etc. A Clerk of the Yard was also appointed to keep accounts and act as property officer, as a subordinate of the Agent. Superintendents, all naval officers, were appointed to supervise the construction and to see that the frigates were built to official specifications, serving somewhat as would the chief inspector in a modern yard. Next, Constructors were appointed, subordinate to the Superintendents. The Constructors, or master builders, were to carry out the construction according to plans and specifications. The Constructor might be said to have been the yard foreman or yard manager in a modern yard.

It is apparent that Knox established very tight control over all procurement, through countersigned purchase orders by the appointed management officials. This prevented any unauthorized procurement by any individual. Strict attendance in the yards by each management official was specifically required by Knox. This tight control should be kept in mind.

The term "rebuilt" will appear often in this discussion. The practice of rebuilding old, rotten, or unsatisfactory men-of-war into new ships—sometimes with extensive changes in hull form, dimensions, armament, and rating or class—seems to have become common in the British Navy during the 17th century. The purpose was to obtain a replacement of a worn-out ship, using maintenance funds instead of money allotted to new construction. The Royal Navy records of the early 18th century show some ships to have been rebuilt twice in less than twenty years, usually with such extensive changes in each "rebuilding" as to show, beyond doubt, that an entirely new vessel had resulted in nearly every case.

Rebuilding began by hauling the ship ashore and stripping her of plank to open the hull to a thorough inspection. If the frames were extensively rotten, a new design was usually prepared and a new ship built. If, however, only a part of the frames were rotten, a very extensive repair might result with no change in dimensions though, usually, there were some changes in appearance and, occasionally, in rate or class.

Repairing the frame of a badly rotted ship often produced difficulty, particularly in joining new work to old. Partial rebuilding could also be expensive; it was shown that the costs of removing numerous rotten timbers were as much as the costs of new work. The Royal Navy also found that unless every infected timber had been removed, rot would soon appear in the new work. It is a matter of record that ships having a "great repair," or those partially rebuilt, in the Royal Navy had short lives in service in most instances.

In the United States Navy, the first vessel to be rebuilt was the 28-gun frigate *Adams,* which had been built at New York in 1799. This was a sharp-model vessel that had seen some hard service at sea. She had been laid up in the Washington dockyard as a result of the reduction in force ordered by President Jefferson and had become unserviceable. A little before the War of 1812 she was hauled ashore, cut in two amidships, and pulled apart 15 feet, and a new section of hull inserted, then torn down and her topsides rebuilt to make her a flush-decked sloop-of-war. (For many years thereafter, as reported in Theodore Roosevelt's *Naval War of 1812,* Navy men often claimed that the *Adams* was not alike on both sides. This was due to the difficulty in joining new to old structure. This partial rebuilding was done to restore a partly sound, old frigate so as to obtain an effective sloop-of-war. To prevent capture, the *Adams* was burned in the Penobscot in 1813.

In April 1816 Congress passed an act for the gradual improvement of the Navy. Though this provided authorization for six 74-gun ships and nine 44-gun frigates, the act did not provide funds. This prevented immediate implementation of the act; after two years funds were granted sufficient only to allow construction to start on the 74s and three of the 44s. In 1820 small vessels were required and four schooners were built using funds originally intended for the larger ships. Some of the 74s were not launched until after midcentury, and this was true of some of the frigates also. Construction of the vessels was paced by the availability of funds—and Congress became less and less generous, as the lessons of the War of 1812 were gradually forgotten—so it was about 15 years before all the keels were laid for the authorized vessels.

Insufficient funds were allotted to the maintenance of all the old ships to keep them in serviceable condition. This was most apparent in the ships built during the War of 1812, where green timber had been used in construction. It was eventually decided to gather together funds, authorized for maintenance, to allow building of replacements for these decaying vessels, while neglecting continuous maintenance of the other much-decayed ships. This "rebuilding" would not require additional authorizations from Congress, nor a request for new construction funds, beyond those required for the authorized vessels under the act of 1816. Were this not done the act of 1816 would have reduced the Navy, since the authorized ships were so delayed in construction. This situation was no secret in Washington.

In 1820 the sloop *Erie*, built at Baltimore in 1813, was surveyed and found to be in poor condition owing to rot in her frames. Sufficient funds were found, so it was decided to rebuild her, adding about four feet amidships, making her 122 feet between perpendiculars. When work began, the difficulties in attaching new work to old led to the gradual replacement of most of the sound old structure, and again the practical difficulties met with in retaining any of the old structure were apparent.

The 117-foot 11-inch sloop-of-war *Peacock* was also in poor condition. Built hurriedly in New York in 1813, she had seen hard service and was severely infected with rot. In 1827 it was decided to "rebuild" her; however, in the light of the experience with her near-sister *Erie* and her condition, it was decided to build a new ship in the process. A new design was drawn by Samuel Humphreys, the chief constructor. This design was prepared in 1827, when the old ship was broken up, and in 1828 the new ship was laid down; she measured 118 feet between perpendiculars and was in all respects a new vessel in design and construction when launched. No attempt was made to retain any material from the old ship, in spite of her notable career, for the ship's construction was for a practical requirement; sentiment did not enter into the matter.

In 1829 the frigates *John Adams, Macedonian,* and *Congress* were in a deteriorated state. Orders were issued to "rebuild" the *John Adams*. It was obvious that this ship, built in 1799 as a 28-gun frigate at Charleston, South Carolina, 139 feet between perpendiculars, was not worth extensive repair. It was also found that the accumulated maintenance funds that had been allotted to her were not only insufficient to rebuild a frigate, the available money could only produce a ship sloop 110 feet long. This was not satisfactory, so other maintenance funds were tapped to allow a 2nd class sloop-of-war (of the 1825 class) 127 feet long to be built. The old ship was broken up in the Norfolk Navy Yard and the new *John Adams* was built there. With this ship, the practice of "rebuilding" had developed to the point where it could produce a ship of larger or smaller dimensions, and of a different class or rating than the original ship.

Next the prize frigate *Macedonian*, 158 feet long, was taken in hand. Though built of the highly touted English oak, she was in a very rotten condition. It was decided to "rebuild" her as a small 36-gun, double-banked (complete battery on spar deck) frigate, 164 feet between perpendiculars. Humphreys prepared her design in 1829. Lack of funds caused a nearly 3-year delay, but she was laid down at Norfolk in 1832 and launched four years later. The old prize frigate thus "rebuilt" was not broken up until the winter of 1835–36. The new *Macedonian,* though 164 feet long, was too small for her armament and soon the guns on the spar deck were removed. Between 1849 and 1852 she was "razeed" or cut down to a spar-decked corvette of 24 guns.

Congress at this time had authorized a somewhat larger naval appropriation, part of which was used in "rebuilding" the *Macedonian* and also in "rebuilding" the prize-ship sloop *Cyane* in 1834. *Cyane* was a complete departure in design from the prize ship and was built as a flush-decked corvette 132 feet 3 inches between perpendiculars.

The *Congress* was rebuilt in 1839. The old 164-foot frigate was broken up in 1836 and the design for the replacement was made that year. She was laid down early in 1839 at the Portsmouth Navy Yard and was built rapidly, being launched in 1841. The rebuilt *Congress* was 179 feet between perpendiculars and was a double-banked frigate. This ship in no way resembled the old *Congress* of 1795–97.

The *Constellation* was the next "rebuilding"; the ship was "rebuilt" 1853–55 at Norfolk, and what then occurred will be described later.

A number of ships had been razeed, including the 74-gun *Independence* which was cut down one deck and made into a frigate, and the frigate *Cumberland,* cut down to a spar-decked corvette. None of these was lengthened. The 74-gun *Franklin* was also to be razeed to a frigate but, upon survey, was found to be too rotten to be cut down. She was broken up at Portsmouth Navy Yard in 1853 and "rebuilt" as a large screw steam-frigate 265 feet 9 inches long and was not launched until 17 September 1864. Bennett says she was built entirely with maintenance funds and it was ten years after laying down that she was ready for machinery.[11]

It will be seen that the rebuildings after 1820 were not "great repairs" and alterations in old ships; rather, the so-called rebuildings were in fact new construction in every instance. This practice produced "modern," effective ships which were the Navy's greatest need. This practice continued for some years after the Civil War.[12] As pointed out earlier, the act for the "Gradual Increase of the Navy" of 1816 actually would have reduced the effective force of the Navy through long delays, imposed by lack of funds, in completing new ships had not administrative "rebuilding" been established as a policy. The lack of Congressional support of the Navy and the long opposition to naval appropriations by Western and Southern congressmen would have usually prevented any increased amount of additional construction funds being authorized, to add to the 1816 program, and often there were insufficient funds for much progress in building ships authorized by the act.

It ought to be made clear that cutting in two amidships and adding a new section, while rebuilding a rotten wood hull, was a difficult operation. The practice in the old wooden shipbuilding yards was first to cut the ship in two at the midsection and pull the hull apart the required distance. Not only did the two halves have to be lined up, the butts and scarphs needed for the rejoining of the hull had to be staggered properly in all longitudinals. When the plank had been stripped from the hull, rotten timbers had to have moulds made of them, before removal, for the replacements. Again, staggered butts in the frame members had to be arranged; as a result, new work had to be far more extensive than that required to build only the added hull section. Removal of old work, without damage to adjoining sound timbers, was often impossible. It is not surprising, then, to find that out of nine cases of United States Navy administrative "rebuilding," only the two earliest ships were intended to retain any of their old structure. Of the remaining seven, there can be no question that six of the "rebuilt" ships were actually new ships, of new design. The other is the *Constellation,* which is in question in this debate.[13]

The Roosevelt Brief

THE EVIDENCE for the Baltimore Committee's claim that the existing *Constellation* is the old frigate of that name was published in an article in the *Maryland Historical Magazine* (vol. 56, no. 1, March 1961, pp. 15–38). It is titled "Yankee Race Horse: The U.S.S. *Constellation*" and the authors are Charles Scarlett, Jr., Leon Polland, John Schneid, and Donald Stewart. The article is basically a brief or memorandum prepared late in 1918 by Franklin Delano Roosevelt, when he was Assistant Secretary of the Navy, which was submitted to Josephus Daniels, Secretary of the Navy. The occasion was a proposal, then under consideration, for the Navy to "restore" the frigate *Constitution* as the oldest American naval vessel afloat. Mr. Roosevelt was in opposition to this proposal, on the grounds that the then existing corvette *Constellation* was in fact the old frigate of that name, built in Baltimore and launched before the *Constitution*. His brief was a presentation of his arguments in support of this claim.

Mr. Roosevelt had developed an interest in American naval history and had prepared a paper on the early American frigates: "Our First Frigates. Some unpublished Facts about Their Construction," which was read at the twenty-second general meeting of the Society of Naval Architects and Marine Engineers, held in New York on 10 and 11 December 1914. This paper was published, with the official plans of the two classes of frigates, in the society's *Transactions*.[14] The matter in question now had not developed in Mr. Roosevelt's mind in 1914, for no mention of it is made in this paper, and the Fox-Humphrey draughts were used.

The brief, or memorandum, submitted to Mr. Daniels was not documented. It consisted of a series of claims flatly stated as facts. The authors, in preparing the article in the *Maryland Historical Magazine*, assembled documentary material which they describe as support for each of the Roosevelt claims, adding, they state, material not known to or used by Mr. Roosevelt. They claim to have collected "a considerable body of documents, copies, plans, drawings and notes." These supporting documents will be discussed later; the Roosevelt brief will first be examined. The authors' foreword or introduction is a version of Roosevelt's basic claims, presented in a series of undocumented statements.

The Roosevelt brief begins with a short account of the building of the frigates authorized in 1794, in which the names of Navy agents and constructors are given. Though the organizational arrangements for building, published in *American State Papers,* are not described, the duties of these men are given in the brief. It is stated there that the Navy agents were responsible for the procurement of labor and material on commission, a fact to be remembered. There follow some erroneous statements about Humphreys, with no mention of Fox but with the dimensions of the vessels given. Obviously Roosevelt had used the *American State Papers* occasionally as a source. A short and incomplete extract from this source regarding the progress reports in contruction of the *Constellation* is also given.

Roosevelt then proceeds to develop his argument that a frigate design by Stodder, the owner of the leased shipyard at Baltimore, was substituted by him for the official design of the *Constellation* class, authorized in 1794. The purpose is to explain the discrepancies in the description and dimensions between the existing corvette and the old frigate, so that it could be apparently established that the corvette is actually the old frigate, slightly altered.

Roosevelt claims that Stodder let it be known that he disagreed with the official design, did not respect Humphreys as a designer, and would accept no orders from Truxtun. The probable source for this would be the Fox Papers, Fox to Truxtun, 2 April 1795. But this is too late a date for any substitution in design, for the timber required in the official design had begun to arrive in the yard. Fox, who had heard of Stodder's alleged statements secondhand, had passed the information on to Truxtun, who in turn passed it on to the War Office. There is no mention in this correspondence of a new design in use or under consideration.

With regard to the mode of the alleged substitution of design, Roosevelt, explains that "Truxtun spent many months with his family, and Major Stodder broke his word; after promising to follow instruction on the building, he changed the entire lower structure of the Constellation. The length when completed was 164 feet, the beam 40 feet but the frame spacing and the structure of the ship which was hidden from view was the work of one David Stodder, the Baltimore builder."

In other words it is inferred that the substitution was accomplished while Truxtun was absent without leave from his post for months at a time so that either he did not see the hull alterations and was unaware of what was going on in lofting and in making the moulds for the substitute design after his return, or was faced with "an accomplished fact" and chose to overlook it. However, Truxtun does not seem in fact to have faced such alternatives, for the Stodder affair did not occur until sometime in March 1795 it is stated, too late for so sweeping a change since most of the timbers were then shaped. Furthermore, "an accomplished fact" could not have existed, for assembly of the frames did not begin until after 14 May 1795, as is shown in the official progress reports, so discrepancies could have been reported in time for correction by the War Office.

It is evident that Roosevelt was unacquainted with the temperament of Truxtun, who was a very proud man, with a keen sense of duty, and who was also meticulous in demanding recognition of his authority. To suggest that this man would stand aside, supinely, in any such situations as have been described, is ludicrous.

Before the arrival of the timber in the shipyard, Truxtun and Stodder were engaged in the construction of the then unusually large building ways, requiring piles and cribbing, and foundations for keel blocks and the groundways. Hence it appears that Stodder could have had no time for the described substitution of design, and all that it entailed in work and time, had the situation described by Roosevelt actually existed.

Roosevelt states that Stodder had received permission to leave out the diagonal riders in the new ship as another evidence of the change of design. Such an omission took place, but not as Stodder's proposal. Truxtun proposed this and managed to get War Office approval. Truxtun also obtained permission to substitute oak for pitch pine deck beams. Actually it was Truxtun who gave Humphreys much trouble with amateur suggestions (Navy Department Records in National Archives, Correspondence on Naval Affairs when Navy was under War Department, 1790–1798) rather than Stodder. This is also apparent in the Fox papers [15] where Truxtun appears to have been often an officious busybody.

Roosevelt states that the *Constellation* was in very poor condition in 1812 as she had been "shot to rot and ruin in her many engagements with the French and Pirates of the Barbary States." She had been damaged in being sunk and raised after she had tailed onto a shoal while at anchor in the Delaware and had fallen on her side and swamped when the tide fell. Aside from the effects of her two battles with French frigates there is no official record yet found of any serious damage from gunfire.

The brief next states that she was "brought up to the main dock," stripped of gear, and "her sides were bolstered and reframed with double planking." Since there was no drydock at Washington she was actually hove down. Truxtun had claimed she was tender, so in this repair she was double-planked or "girdled." This produced an increase in extreme beam of about 14 inches, and a belt of double planking along the hull from some distance abaft the stem to about the quarters aft; the belt was faired at the ends into the entrance and run. This belt extended from a few feet below the light load line to a little above the load waterline, covering the wales. She was the only American naval vessel so treated for stability reasons. No additional timbers were applied to the frames so "moulded beam" remained as before, but "extreme beam" was increased.

The brief then goes on to claim, in curiously nonprofessional language, that the ship was given "new iron works" and that the "old line and wound works" were replaced. It is also claimed that the *Constellation* was "the first ship of the navy to carry

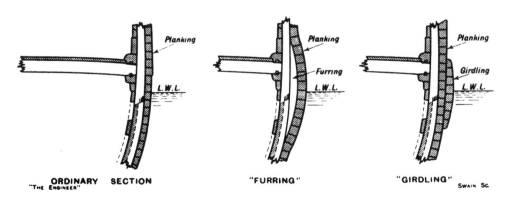

FIGURE 4.—Girdling method employed in *Constellation*. (*The Engineer,* 4 August 1922, p. 109)

iron work on her masts and spars." "Wound work" does not appear in the nautical dictionaries available to the writer, *The Sailor's Word Book: An Alphabetical Digest of Nautical Terms* by Admiral W. H. Smyth, R.N. (Glasgow and Edinburgh, 1867), and *Young Sea Officers Sheet Anchor,* as well as the modern *International Maritime Dictionary;* all agree that bands of hemp rope around built-up masts and spars were called "wooldings," while iron bands, when introduced in the second quarter of the 19th century in place of wooldings, were called "hoops."

It has been accepted that ironwork was late in being introduced into the United States Navy. The earliest evidence yet found shows that iron work increased, replacing hemp, in the 1830s, though some chain rigging had come into use after the War of 1812 in the Navy.

The brief states that Captain Tingey was in charge of the large repair at Washington in 1811–12 and was responsible for work done on the ship. The authors, in their introduction, appear to believe that in this great repair the "tumblehome," or falling-inboard, of the topsides was reduced by Tingey. This would mean complete retopping, which is not mentioned in any records known to the writer and which is contrary to the plans available; drawn later than 1812. Roosevelt makes no mention of this change in tumblehome anywhere in his brief.

The brief has nothing specific about repairs to the ship after 1815. It states that between 1812 and 1848 "she had been overloaded with equipment, men and too many cannon, not to mention some 150 tons of kentledge which had warped her old keel and top keel." In shipbuilding terms she had a hogged keel and keelson. It will be seen later that incorrect terminology in the Roosevelt brief ostensibly originates in the statements made in sources mentioned in the footnotes. The remarkable thing about this is that the sources are alleged to be statements of naval officers, a shipwright, and a naval constructor, all of whom are made responsible for much of the highly unprofessional language and terminology which will be discussed later.

The only reference to repairs in the 1812–48 period is one in 1830–32, "but not as much as the works of 1812." Roosevelt appears to have believed that practically all repair work could be done by the crew at sea.

The brief then describes how Roosevelt thought the vessel was rebuilt at Gosport, or the Norfolk Navy Yard, after surveys in 1852–53. As a result of these surveys it is claimed, it was decided that "part of the hull" could be preserved by rebuilding her as a first-class sloop-of-war. In 1853, the brief states, the ship was dismantled to her spar deck and then, "with the aid of hundreds of men and animals . . . hauled up the blocks covered with tallow and black lead and into one of the huge shiphouses at Gosport Navy Yard." She was then "stripped down to her lower frames and planks which were suitable for reuse. These were calked up [sic] and her keel was spliced, adding some 12 feet to the length of the vessel. Her keel was warped, high in the center and low on the ends." Next, "a shoe or extra keel was made which fastened onto her old keel to straighten it."

This product of Roosevelt's imagination is merely an incorrect and lubberly version of the lengthening operation in a wooden ship, much abbreviated. The ship would actually have spars, rigging, armament, stores, and deck gear, as well as ballast, removed. There would be no need to knock off her bulwarks at this stage.

It did not require hundreds of men and animals to haul her up, the Norfolk Navy Yard had geared capstans and other mechanical aids by this date and, in any case, her "blocks" were not covered with tallow and black lead; instead, her ground-ways were tallowed. No mention is made by Roosevelt of the work required after the hull has been pulled apart and in obtaining the hull form on either side of the cut, for lofting the "insert." Nor is there mention of stripping 15 to 30 feet either side of the cut in order to stagger the butts and scarphs in the longitudinals, or keelson, planking, clamps, stringers, shelves, and ceiling. Roosevelt imagined the hog in the keel of the old frigate would be built into the new vessel. As will be shown, the bottom of her keel had been made straight sometime prior to the surveys in 1853, though the keel rabbet showed about 1 foot 9½ inches of hog. This would have caused deformation in her keelson and in all of longitudinal and upper structural members of the hull. It is evident that Roosevelt was ignorant of the various steps to be taken in lengthening a wooden ship and of the undesirability of hog in the keel, which, in such an extensive repair as Roosevelt imagined, would not be tolerated.

Next, the brief describes the alleged difficulties in the vessel's hull form. "The loftsmen and draftsmen at Gosport had their troubles with the old Constellation as she did not compare with Humphreys' plan of the ship which was drawn in 1795. David Stodder's long forgotten grave held the answers. The Stodder changes of the Constellation and his idea of what a Baltimore ship should have and not have was the problem facing the chiefs of construction at Norfolk."

This whole matter is best discussed when the supporting attempts at documentation are examined. However, the naval constructors would have very readily solved the "troubles," that Roosevelt imagined, by taking the lines off the ship, for in any case so old a vessel would show deformation that would not appear in her building plans. A take-off would then be necessary so that new work would fit the old with the required accuracy.

It is stated in the brief that "some 37 percent of the Constellation still remains in Newport. She has her stem, original keel excepting one section forward, most of her oak frames are still intact and some 136 tons of old wrought iron [sic] kentledge still strings along her hold. She retains knees from the hackmatack [sic] brought up in boats in 1796." These statements are ridiculous. There was, and is, no way of determining the exact age of timber in the corvette. Certainly the corvette could not have her "original keel excepting one section forward" if she had been cut in two and lengthened as claimed elsewhere by Roosevelt, for this cut would have to be amidships, or at the "dead flat" in that vicinity .

Carbon tests are useless in determining the age of the timbers in the vessel. She has existed, between 1855 and the present, 113 years, and the appearance of her timbers could readily give the impression of great age. "Dated" timbers and metal fastenings are said to have been found in both *Constellation* and *Constitution* but it is naive to accept these as evidence. Vintage wood and fastenings are the byproducts of numerous repairs and overenthusiasm on the part of workmen. Curiously enough, only famous ships seem to have "vintage" material. Kentledge is pig iron, not wrought iron. Hackmatack, or larch, is not found in Maryland nor in Georgia nor in the Carolinas; it is native to the northeastern states. No larch was used in the Baltimore frigate nor in the corvette, both of which were built of white and live oak, yellow pine, and, in the frigate, a little red cedar which was employed according to the specifications.[16]

Further, Roosevelt states: "The Constellation has Stodder's building still on board [sic] and she is in fact the same ship built in Baltimore in 1795." He also claims that "she is still the same clipper type Constellation" and repeats the claim that "Humphreys' hull and mould plan was changed by Stodder and all that was evident of change in 1797 was her thinned-out bow (clipper-type). Stodder did not suffer from this but was of high degree in his futuristic thinking and design [sic]. The Constitution was of sufficient length to convert her to a sloop of war several years after Constellation's rebuilding. Constitution like the Constellation was rebuilt many times but did not have her length altered."

It is not true, of course, that either the frigate or the existing corvette was very sharp in the entrance; neither supports any claim of "futuristic thinking" in "high degree" either in 1794–95 or in 1853–55; plans that have been published prove that again and again. *Constitution* was never cut down in structure to a corvette, though in the 1850s she had her quarterdeck and forecastle guns removed. No especial length was required for a corvette rating. As in sloops-of-war, the rating corvette meant a vessel armed on one deck only.

It is only fair to acknowledge that the *Constellation* Committee, or the authors of "Yankee Race Horse," were sportsmanlike in publishing Josephus Daniels' rather facetious reply to Roosevelt's brief; parts relating to the *Constellation* follow:

December 18, 1918

To—Roosevelt, disciple of John Paul Jones

So the off-sets for the present Constellation were taken from the lower structure of the old ship and these were laid out on the mold loft floor with an extension of 12 feet to the body. Now that you have proved your point and made everyone in construction mad at you, do you want the ship on the Hudson for a Christmas present.

I am,

Sincerely yours,
(Signed)   Josephus Daniels
(Secretary of the Navy)

It seems evident that Daniels had consulted the Bureau of Construction and Repair and they had evaluated the Assistant Secretary's unsound claims regarding the *Constellation*. At any rate, the decision was made to restore the *Constitution* (instead of the *Constellation*) after the Roosevelt brief had been examined.

Documentation of the Roosevelt Brief

T HE FIRST FOOTNOTE to be discussed in the documentation of the Roosevelt brief is that referring to sources used by the authors. They state (*M.H.M.*, pp. 17–18) that "All research into early American naval history has been severely hampered since the complete destruction by fire of the Newport Naval Training Station Museum, January 25, 1946. Lost in this disaster were the Theodore Roosevelt Collection of Naval Papers relating to the War of 1812, some 300 early ship plans, and hundreds of original letters and documents, which included the bulk of documentary records pertaining to the *Constellation* possessed by the Navy Department." This footnote goes on to say that the authors made use of the copies of these documents "made in years prior to the fire, as well as work done by other researchers from the originals."

There seems to be some confusion in references to this source for, in "Abbreviations for Sources," the authors give "NWCL" as *"Constellation* File, Library of Naval War College, U.S. Naval Training Station, Newport, R.I." It will be noticed that the source named first is "Naval Training Station Museum," while in Mr. Polland's paper the source is placed in "Barracks B," "Constellation File." It is strange that the exact location of such an important source for the support of their cause should be in doubt, to this extent, in the minds of the authors or of Franklin D. Roosevelt.

An investigation carried out at the U.S. Naval Station in April 1967 showed that certain *Constellation* records, covering the period 1883 to 1941, had been transferred to the National Archives on microfilm. In December 1958 logs and general correspondence regarding *Constellation* in the years 1894 to 1906 had been transferred. Investigation also showed that none of this material referred to the matter in debate. It should be noted that the *Constellation* was assigned to Newport in 1894.

There are some *"Constellation* History Records," including a history of the station, in the files. Examination of these shows them to have been prepared in 1932, 1936, and 1937, and to be of a popular nature, without documentation. No material relating to the 1797–1855 period building and repairs records could be found, with the exceptions described later. The material sent to Washington included some material dated before the time given for the destruction of the *Constellation* files at Newport.

Certain facts came to light during the investigation (24 April 1967) at the Naval War College and at the Naval Station. The first of these is that the Naval War College Library was never destroyed by fire. There never was a "Naval War College Museum" nor a "Naval Training Station Museum." The Naval Training Station Library was in "The House that Jack Built," next to Barracks "B," and was not burned with the latter building in 1946. Personnel employed in the libraries have no knowledge of any collection of original plans or documents, nor of the "Theodore Roosevelt Collection of Naval Papers." In fact, Theodore Roosevelt apparently made but three short visits to the station, according to records there, and no one could suggest any reason why he would have placed such a collection in so inconvenient a place for his use. There is no record to be found of the storage of any documents by the libraries in Barracks "B." The fire that destroyed this building broke out at 11:28 p.m., 19 January 1946, not 25 January 1946. Four lives were lost in the building, which contained quarters for recruits and station personnel. The office and records of the Chaplain, the American Red Cross, Navy Relief, Public Information, and the files of the *Navalog*, a station news publication, were destroyed.[17]

The "300 early ship plans," apparently wholly naval vessels, cannot be accounted for. The plan files of the Bureau of Construction and Repair, now in Navy Records, National Archives, do not show this number of plans to have been possible for naval vessels built earlier than 1850, considering the total number of naval vessels built from 1793 on and the plans now preserved there.[18] The official plan files would be the only source for what is described as the "Theodore Roosevelt Collection."

There is nothing in Theodore Roosevelt's *Naval War of 1812*[19] nor in his contribution to *The Royal Navy, A History from the Earliest Times to the Present* (vol. 6, Wm. Laird Clowes, and others: Boston and London, 1901) that indicates his possession of so much technical material, for he does not refer to draughts or plans in his possession in his discussions of the size of American men-of-war. Since the *Constellation* did not play an active part in the War of 1812 it is difficult to understand why Theodore Roosevelt would have any special interest in her which would lead him to extract a large file of plans and documents, relative to this ship, from the Bureau files.

While there are small collections of naval shipbuilding papers, not part of the Bureau files, these are plans and papers that were in the hands of naval constructors upon their retirement. The largest known is John Lenthall's collection in the Franklin Institute in Philadelphia. Much of this collection is plans that are duplicated in the Bureau files, the whole amounting to less than ten naval vessels.

Still another oddity is that file copies of the alleged official correspondence, from the "Naval War College Library" collection that is cited, cannot be found in the War Office, nor in Navy Department correspondence files, whether incoming or outgoing.

To proceed with this examination of the authors' footnotes to the Roosevelt brief. The next to be taken up is in support of the situation described there, which allowed Stodder to depart from the official design (*M.H.M.*, footnote 18, p. 21). It begins: " '. . . did not agree . . .' is a mild description of Stodder's attitude. Joshiah [sic] Fox wrote to Truxtun (April 2, 1795 . . .) passing on the second-hand but none the less rousing information that Stodder was 'contemptuous' of the whole proceedings. The Baltimore Constructor maintained he could do a much better job of drafting and moulding a frigate than Humphreys. According to Fox's informant,

Stodder declared he would follow neither draught nor moulds nor any directions from the War Office, and that he would not take orders from any officer in his yard."

Truxtun is said by the authors to have reported this to Pickering, who replied, 7 April 1795, "making it clear that Knox's arrangements . . . gave any Superintendent full authority to enforce the Government's plan of building. Truxtun would have the power to discharge the Constructor as an extreme measure, but he was urged instead to smooth matters out." This would seem to settle the matter decisively. But the footnote goes on to state that Pickering wrote Stodder, "devoting a lengthy opening paragraph to the fact than an 'important personage' had been 'rendered uneasy in his position,' and stressed the importance of maintaining 'harmony' at all costs. . . . The balance of the letter affirms that the plans of construction adopted by the War Department are to be exactly followed unless advantageous suggestions are made, in which case prior Department approval will be sought."

On this evidence the authors somehow conclude that Pickering not only knew of the substitution in the design but had approved of it, with Fox's concurrence. Obviously Pickering was merely trying to keep peace in the yard and following a commonsense administrative procedure. So far, no record of Fox having any information regarding a substitution in design has been found in his papers. In plain terms Stodder was informed that the official plans and building program must be followed, though the Secretary would consider any suggestion for improvement, provided it was submitted to his office and approved before being carried out, which would allow a proposal to be submitted to his technical advisers. He certainly would not pass judgment himself, "off the cuff." Attention is invited to the time factor—by the time of this incident and correspondence, timber for the authorized design was coming into the yard. So it was far too late for any change in hull design. While a great many proposals for "improvements" on the ships were offered, the small number that were approved—dealing mostly with structure—show that in the main the official program was adhered to in building. There was no room for any casual, irresponsible changing of design.

The reports on progress show that by 14 May 1795, the keel and keelson timbers were in the Baltimore yard, along with most of the live oak which at this date had been "shaped to moulds and bevels." This represented weeks of work, perhaps months. At any rate, the existence of a change in design cannot be shown possible unless it occurred in the fall of 1794, to allow time for this timber (for the unauthorized design) to reach the yard and be worked. There is no claim or evidence either by Roosevelt or by the authors that any change in design was even contemplated by Stodder so early; the whole claim is based on a situation said to have occurred in the spring of 1795.

Another problem in the introduction of a substitute design by Stodder would be timber. As the Knox organization plan showed, Stodder had neither money nor authority to buy timber. Even though his design might use some timber reworked from the official program stock, it would require quite a lot of new timber if the design were to differ from the official draught enough to resemble the corvette's hull form, as claimed by Roosevelt. Where would such timber come from and how would it be paid for?

The situation Roosevelt tried to establish was that the substitution in design was possible because of Truxtun's long absences from the yard, allowing Stodder to do as he pleased. It has been pointed out that Roosevelt obviously knew little about Truxtun and his character. Now follows a footnote evidence from the alleged "Naval War College Library" collection. This is said to be dated 14 April 1795, Stodder to Truxtun, and follows: ". . . I must say to you, Sir, that I have all of my facilities, and for your information *I have Mr. Pickering's authority to change the draughts and moulds of this frigate.* (Italics by Committee) Mr. Humphreys, I must remind you has had little experience in building other than merchant ships . . . and he being a quaker shoud' be catholic [sic] in his design of ships of war. I have been in agreement with the War Office . . . besides even you have disagreed with Humhpreys on more than one occasion. I beg you not to write to Humphreys of this matter as Mr. Pickering will tell you he agrees with me as does the brothers here on materials and instructions. I also ask that you act more in the manner befiting a masonic brother and show some amount of trust in your fellows. I am with respect, David Stodder."

To anyone who has read much about Truxtun, it is impossible to believe that he would have received such an impertinent and foolish letter from a subordinate without a violent explosion of temper, action, and correspondence. Any claim that Stodder had Pickering's authority to change the plan would be fiction, for no such grant can be found in the Department papers. Humphreys had worked with Wharton in building *Randolph* during the Revolution and had built and repaired vessels for Truxton, so was well known to him. On the other hand Stodder had not built any man-of-war, and a search of the Baltimore registry did not produce any record of a merchant vessel over 600 register tons built by him, while the frigate was over 1200 register tons. Humphreys' association with Wharton was well known to all. It is obvious that the person who composed this piece of evidence did not know Truxtun's character, nor much about Humphreys' career.

Another example from the same source, *M.H.M.,* (footnote 21, p. 22) is an alleged letter, Pickering to Stodder, of 18 May 1795: "I have asked all the builders to communicate with me on new ideas which will benefit the Frigates. Mr. Humphreys may protest, but *I assure you I will support your changes in the molds and design* [sic].[20]—You are the second person to inform me of Humphreys protests and I must remind Mr. Humphreys of his status and of the considerations I have given the builders, to improve his ships. I have informed him that you are the owner of a navy-yard and also a master-builder *and that your changes as displayed in your model are in accord with Mr. Fox and the War Office* . . . " (Italics by the Committee).

This "document" is an obvious absurdity for, as all concerned (including Pickering) well knew, Humphreys owned a "navy yard" or shipyard, and was a "master-builder" or master-shipwright. Finally Pickering was not a complete fool and would not have taken on such responsibilities in so off-hand a manner. There is, of course, no record of Fox being "in accord," as said before. No copy of this "letter" has been found in Humphreys' papers nor in the War Department files in National Archives. Were such letters sent, as the alleged communication indicates, there would be file copies in the Department records, as also has been said before.

This is the first mention of a model of Stodder's design which seems to infer a half model had been sent to the War Office. A diligent search has been made to find some reference to such a model in the War Department correspondence without success. One would expect to find an accompanying explanation of the half model's superiority in form over the official design, along with the Department's approval. Of course the half model would not shorten the time required to employ a substitute frigate design carried to the launching stage.

In the same footnote there is a claim that a change was made in frame spacing in the substitute frigate, though why this should be done is not explained. This claim is based on a letter, quoted by the authors, in the Pickering papers, Historical Society of Pennsylvania, Stodder to Pickering, suggesting a cheaper way to bolt the floor timbers and incidentally referring to the frame spacing being 32 inches. In the official draught the frame spacing was 26 inches. It was apparent, of course, that if the spacing was changed, to 32 inches, new moulds and timbers would have to be substituted for those of the official design. Furthermore, the frames would be fewer in number. To correct the increased weakness that this would produce, there could be an increase in thickness of planking and ceiling, or wider frame futtocks, none of which is mentioned in the footnotes, but all requiring timber not specified in the official program. There is a simple explanation to all of this—Stodder made a mistake in his letter to Pickering.

Mention is made (*M.H.M.*, footnote 20, p. 22) of a plan in the Records of the Bureau of Construction and Repair, Navy Records, National Archives, C&R 107–13–4B, which the authors state was made from "Bureau records," without giving any reason for this conclusion. Instead, the authors direct attention to a pencil sketch on the drawing showing frame spacing of 32 inches and marked "Old." This sketch is obviously an addition, for the original plan is in ink. This sketch is used to support the claim that the frigate had the increased frame spacing, as well as a change in hull form to that of the corvette.

This plan, "Transverse Sections of Frigate Constellation, Scale ¼ of an inch = one foot, Norfolk, Feb. 1853," shows nine half-sections with dimensions (offsets) drawn in ink, indexed C&R 107–13–4B. With it is plan C&R 107–13–4A, which the authors do not mention. The latter plan is of the keel of the frigate *Constellation* showing the amount of hog in the keel rabbet—about 1 foot 9½ inches—with height measurements at fixed points given. The false keel, shoe, or bottom of the keel had been made straight. Its title is "Constellation, Scale ¼ of an inch = one foot," and written on this drawing is "Received January 1853," with "from Norfolk, Va." added in pencil. The nine sections have, as a common base line, the straight bottom of the keel, so the sections stand from one another the height of the hog at each station, as drawn in C&R 107–13–4A. The nine sections in C&R 107–13–4B have the recorded offsets taken from outboard, vertical heights from individual base lines referenced to the bottom of the keel, to comply with the hog at each section. The vertical offsets are two feet apart. The vertical reference line is 21 feet 7½ inches outboard from the hull centerline. On this, the horizontal offsets are recorded at 2-foot intervals referenced to the hog line so that the individual level lines of all of the sections are not on the same plane longitudinally. The plan is a record of the taking-off of the lines of the old Baltimore frigate, with take-off sections spaced 20 feet apart, except the end sections which are 10 feet from their neighbors. That

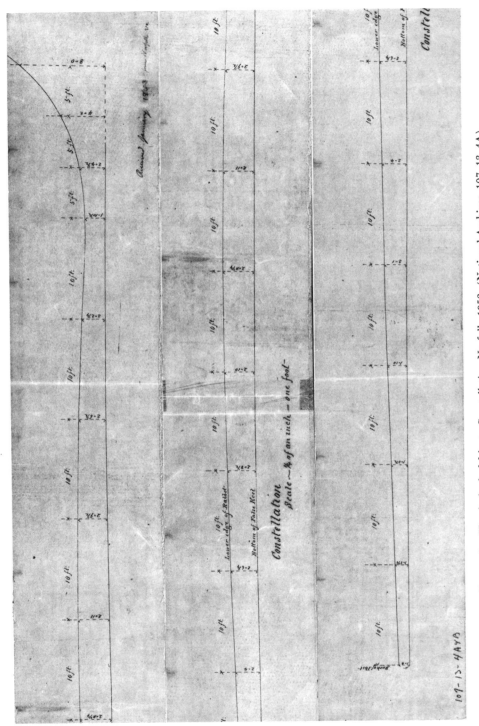

FIGURE 6.—Hog in keel of frigate *Constellation*, Norfolk, 1853. (National Archives, 107–13–4A)

the plan is a take-off is shown by the measurements, or offsets, being taken from outboard and by the use of the hogged keel rabbet drawing to establish the heights of each section. The plan was probably made when planking was stripped from the hull, and was intended to inform the Bureau of the hull distortions resulting from excessive hog.

An overlay of the midsection of the frigate of 1794–95 was drawn on ¼ inch= one foot scale from the offsets formerly in the Fox papers at Salem and placed over the section in C&R 107–13–4B identified as being "6'7" forward of after side of port No. 6" which was 2 feet 3 inches forward of the 1794 offset midsection ⊕, but where the dead flat had begun. This is shown in Figure 7 and it will be seen that the topsides practically coincide while the bottoms of the sections show a slight difference. Whether the slight variations are the result of errors in measurements or inaccurate plotting by myself, the similarity is sufficient to prove that C&R 107X–13–4B is a takeoff of the old frigate, made at Norfolk before February 1853. This shows beyond question

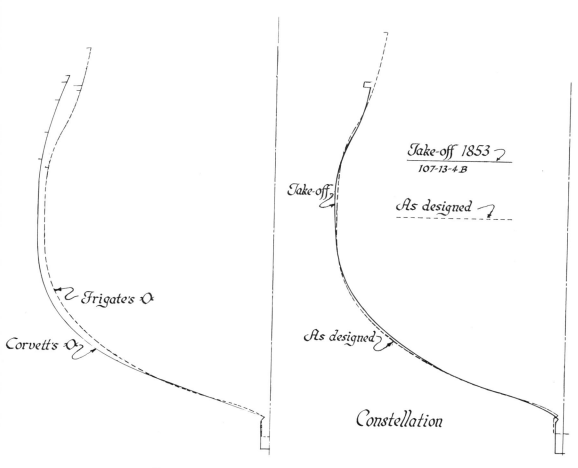

FIGURE 7.—Overlay of midsections of *Constellation*.

that the old frigate was different in form from the corvette and, furthermore, that the old frigate existed until, at least, early 1853. The moulded beam shown in C&R 107–13–4B is that of the old frigate and not that of the corvette. This supports the claim that the ship was merely double-planked at the waterline in 1811–12 and that her frames in the topsides were not altered. The sketch of the 32-inch frame spacing, marked "old," cannot be accounted for in this drawing, unless it is going to be claimed that the 32-inch spacing was used in building to the 1794 design! Otherwise why show it on this drawing? If this question cannot be answered intelligently, the remaining possibility is that someone has tried to tamper with the official records.

In the same footnote regarding the claim that increased frame spacing was used by Stodder, it is stated "That a change in shape did occur is substantiated by a letter from Truxtun to a member of the House of Representatives (Truxtun to Livingston, 22 May 1798 NWCL): . . . 'I must say though we probably have a better ship through the efforts of Major David Stodder—the constructor here . . . his new ideas in the form of the bow will most likely increase the speed through the water of the hull'."

In Truxtun's correspondence after the *Constellation* went to sea there are complaints about her sharpness, which reduced her stowage (this seems to mean sharp deadrise). In *Naval Documents Related to the Quasi-War Between the United States and France, Naval Operations* (Office of Naval Records and Library, Government Printing Office, Washington, 1935, p. 517, Truxtun to Secretary of the Navy, 26 March 1799), Truxtun refers to the matter thus: "these ships [proposed 74-gun ships] must have great room and not be over-sharp as our frigates certainly are." This makes it plain that he is referring to deadrise in all the 1794 frigates being too great, which reduced stowage. In no captain's correspondence is there mention of a remarkably sharp entrance in *Constellation*. The deadrise and deep draft of the frigates were considered objectionable by Fox and Truxtun, as the Fox papers at Salem make abundantly clear.

The purpose of the "Naval War College Library" composition is to show that the old frigate had been built as "sharp" in the bow as the corvette, and so was an innovation in 1794–95. This is untrue, as the many published plans of vessels of 1790–1850 show, for neither frigate nor corvette had such sharp ends as some of the earlier vessels, and at Baltimore there were many very sharp-ended "Baltimore Clippers" that made either the frigate, or the corvette for that matter, look full in comparison.

It is also stated (*M.H.M.,* Footnote 23, p. 23) that "Josiah Fox in later life wrote extensively about his activities in the early Navy, and left a document entitled 'Sworn statement J. Fox—in the year 1835' (NWCL) crediting himself and Doughty with the drafting of virtually all the major Naval vessels of the first period of construction, except the *Constellation,* as follows: '. . . vessels of 36 guns—Congress and Crescent built to Algeria [sic] (Constellation drafted by Stodder).'" For some reason the full "document" has never been published. Mr. Polland, in his 1966 paper, p. 13, refers to the "document" as follows: "From the Naval War College at Newport, R. I. 'Barracks B' came a copy of a sworn document by Josiah Fox contemporary and former subordinate of Humphreys. This document, burned in the disastrous fire at the installation, had fortunately been transcribed in a typewritten sheet and is thus preserved. It lists ships, including the original fleet actually designed by himself, including, he says none by Humphreys and '*Constellation* designed by Stodder.' This document is considered by CRC [*Constellation* Research Committee] to be 'questionable' in its present form as it could well have been subjected to the 'license' of the transcriber. It should, however, be taken at its face value and is thus recorded." A very surprising conclusion, reached on the admittedly doubtful "document."

Attention is invited to the reference of a new site for the Newport records. The Naval War College had no relationship to "Barracks B," nor did the latter have any relationship to the Naval Training Station Library. Again, according to statements made at the Naval Station (formerly the Naval Training Station) there is no record to be found of library material or plans being in any storeroom in Barracks B.

There are statements by Josiah Fox regarding his services that the authors, or Mr. Franklin D. Roosevelt, did not cite. A very complete statement is in the Fox Papers, Peabody Marine Museum, Salem, Massachusetts. A transcript of this document, with some annotation of doubtful value by Wesson, is in *A Calendar of the Papers of Josiah Fox in the Collection of Ernest J. Wesson,* cited earlier. Fox's statement of services was addressed to Samuel Southard, Secretary of the Navy, on 27 November 1826, with supporting documents. In this he first gave a full account of his participation in the frigate building program and of his later services as naval constructor. Next he stated: "The four frigates which the Subscriber draughted were, The United States, Constitution, Constellation, and the one intended to have been built a Norfolk. [The Chesapeake]." He also stated that live oak previously prepared at Norfolk "had been taken to finish the frigate Constellation." Since the Norfolk ship was one of the three 36s on the official draught it is obvious that the official design was used for the Baltimore frigate since the timbers on official design moulds could be used. The statement of service is signed by Fox and dated 27 November 1826 "near Wheeling, Va." Appended to it was the following: "Ships of War draughted by Josiah Fox" "Frigates of 44 guns": [sic]

44 United States
44 Constitution
44 Philadelphia
44 Cheasapeake
36 Constellation
36 Crescent (built for Dey of Algiers)
32 John Adams
22 Portsmouth
18 Hornet
18 Wasp
12 Ferret
and a great part of the numerous gunboats."

In 1827 a controversy arose between Fox and Samuel Humphreys (Chief Constructor, U.S.N., and son of Joshua Humphreys) over the credit for the designs of the authorized frigates. The frigate *United States* had beaten the French frigate *Lafayette* in a sailing race, and an account of this had been published in the *Niles Weekly Register,* 18 August 1827, along with a reprint of a traveler's interview with Fox that had been published in the *Wheeling Gazette,* in which Fox had made certain claims. Soon after this, Samuel Humphreys published a letter in the *National Journal* belittling Fox's claims and promoting his father's. An account of this controversy, with transcripts of three unfinished drafts of Fox's reply to Samuel Humphreys, was published by Mr. Merle T. Westlake Jr., as "Josiah Fox Gentleman, Quaker and Shipbuilder." [21]

The most complete draft was transcribed by Mr. Westlake to read:

I observed in Niles Register of the 18th ultimo That Mr. Samuel Humphreys states that the extract of a letter from a Gentleman on his travels in the Western Country which appeared in the Wheeling Gazette is incorrect & asserts that the Original drafts of the Frigates United States, Constitution, President, Consellation & Congress—were drawn by Joshua Humphreys of Philada [sic] agreeably to Dimensions proposed by that Gent'n to Gen'l Knox the Secretary of War & that the only part Mr. Fox took in the Business was making Copies from the Originals. He is willing to give to Mr. F. all the Credit that is due him & with that disposition states that Mr. F. drafted the Frigates Philada & Chesapeake & the sloop Wasp and built the two last named Vessels.

If Mr. S. H. had sufficiently informed himself before he undertook to give publicity to those assertions I feel Confident that he would not have brought them before the View of the Public. I have always entertained a great respect for the Gentleman but he was only a school Boy at the time & consequently unacquainted with the true state of the Business connected with those ships I feel disposed to pass over his assertion that the statement was "incorrect."

It never came to my knowledge who gave Gen'l Knox the first or original dimensions for those Frigates, it only remains for me to say that I opposed them—& that Gen'l Knox by my advice altered the dimensions of the 44 Gun Frigates those of the 36 Gun Frigates may have been as first proposed. That the drafting of the Frigates was Confided to me as well as laying them down in the Mould loft & making the Moulds &, all of which was done by my advice & assistance. Mr. J. H. did attempt to palm drafts upon me as the approved ones but General Knox having reced [sic] intimation of the Circumstance did in a public manner not only reject them but laid an additional responsibility on me that I should undiviatingly adhere to my drafts as being the original ones approved by him. There may be Gentlemen yet living who can testify to those facts if required. Mr. J. H.'s drafts & Models were not only rejected by the Secretary of War but by all the Master Ship Builders from Swedes Church to upper part of Kensington, to whom they were submitted.

The other and less complete drafts are variations of the foregoing and relate only to the controversy over credit for the frigate designs. It will be seen that Fox claimed he made the draughts for the frigates and does not mention the Stodder design for *Constellation.*

The nearest thing to a "Sworn Statement" found yet in any of the Fox papers is a document published by Elizabeth B. Stanton, "Josiah Fox's Story of the Nation's First Navy, An attested copy of his record in the Navy which was Submitted by Him to the Navy Department Shortly before his Death—Transcript made for *The Journal of American History* by his great-great granddaughter." [22] It was "attested' only so far as the transcript was "a true copy" of course, and not sworn to by Fox, who was a Quaker, by the way, and would not "take oath" but might "affirm." This is a version of the statement of service published in *Wesson's Calendar;* which one was employed in Fox's letter to the Secretary of the Navy has yet to be determined; the Stanton version, as published, has supporting documents attached to it, also.

The pertinent statements in the Stanton version are on the first page of the published transcript "The subscriber drafted the 'United States,' 'Constellation' and the one intended to have been built at Norfolk and Mr. Doughty drafted the 'President' and 'Congress'." There is the same list of ships that Fox stated he designed in the document in the *Wesson Calendar,* now in the Fox papers at Salem. Fox, therefore, specifically stated that he designed *Constellation* and nowhere mentions Stodder, nor his draught, nor model, in his statement of service of 1826, nor in the drafts for his reply to Samuel Humphreys in 1827.

The "Naval War College Library" collection, cited in the remaining footnotes, includes a "statement by Captain Tingey," Captain of the Washington Navy Yard, December 1811, in which he describes *Constellation* as "very sharp forward," makes reference to her great speed, poor condition, thinness of planking, and speaks of "the flat transom that runs from starboard to larboard and from the taffrail under water to the post." Were it authentic, this curiously unprofessional statement would be the first and apparently the only reference to a peculiar transom on this ship; no other reference to an unusual transom on *Constellation* has yet been found.

Another of the "Naval War College Library documents" is described as "Major Battle Damage, Repairs and Reconstruction to U. S. Ship Constellation 1797–1855," File 1231–A, credited to Admiral W. L. Capps at direction of Truman H. Newberry, Assistant Secretary of Navy, and the authors date this 1905–08. No office file copy has been found in the Navy Department records; this alleged report will be fully examined later when Mr. Polland's paper is discussed.

Still another Tingey "document" is presented, from the "Naval War College Library," in which he uses such terms as "The wound work of the masts," and "iron should be used to provide im-movabl' [sic] strength for masts and booms," which have been noticed in the Roosevelt brief.

Footnote 27 (*M.H.M.,* p. 25) includes the reference: "see NWCL, Statement of Samuel Humphreys 1829 Repairs, for enlargement and rounding of stern" (of the *Constellation*). Since it is alleged that this was among the burned documents, it can hardly be seen! Why the stern should be "enlarged" in order to round it is not explained.

Footnote 29 (M.H.M., p. 25) refers to an alleged change in beam and, apparently, quotes from a Tingey report "to remove excess tumble in the home come [sic] of the ship" in 1812–13. Had such a change in topsides been a fact it would follow that she was "retopped," a very extensive alteration which had no relation to the "girdling" that was certainly done in the 1812 repair. Retopping would not change the moulded beam of a frigate, however; a complete rebuilding would be required to do this. The transverse sections of frigate *Constellation* February 1853 drawing discussed earlier shows that no change in tumble home was made.[23]

In attempting to show that the corvette was the old frigate, altered, the authors put heavy strain on some of the evidence. For example, it is stated (*M.H.M.,* footnote 31, p. 26) that constructor John Lenthall, in a letter to Commodore Skinner 18 Dec. 1851, proposed "to retain her" (inferring that the old vessel's structure was to be retained) whereas the full document in the National Archives (Figure 8) shows no proposal, but rather a question:

If the ancient renoun of this ship makes it desirable to retain her (for in point of economy there will be a loss) the plan heretofore under consideration of the Bureau seems well adapted to carrying it out—This ship has been found deficient in stability (though built from the same lines as the Constitution) but in other respects she is well-formed."

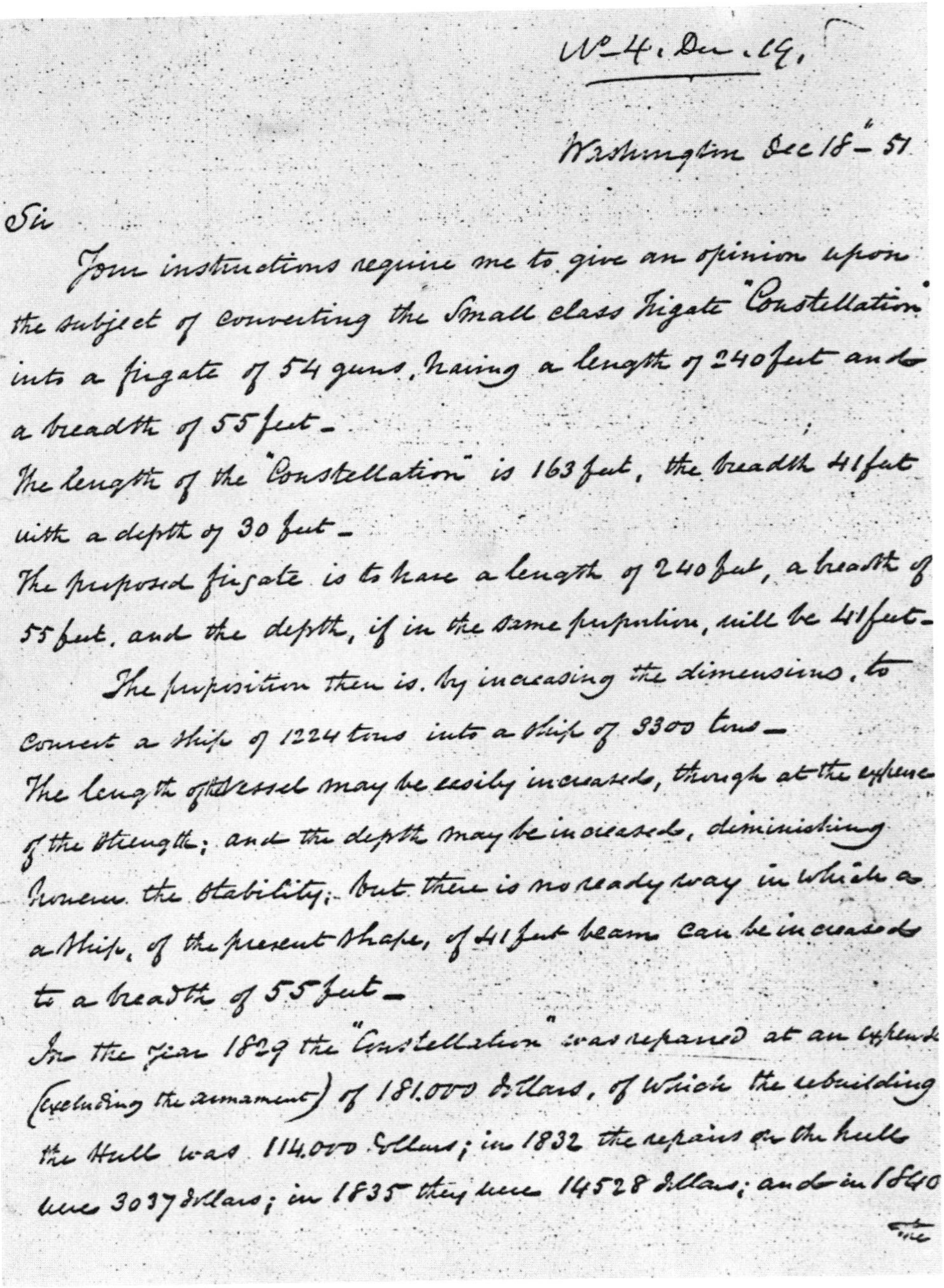

No. 4. Dec. 19,

Washington Dec 18 - 51

Sir

Your instructions require me to give an opinion upon the subject of converting the Small class Frigate "Constellation" into a frigate of 54 guns, having a length of 240 feet and a breadth of 55 feet —

The length of the "Constellation" is 163 feet, the breadth 41 feet with a depth of 30 feet —

The proposed frigate is to have a length of 240 feet, a breadth of 55 feet, and the depth, if in the same proportion, will be 41 feet —

The proposition then is, by increasing the dimensions, to convert a ship of 1224 tons into a ship of 3300 tons —

The length of the vessel may be easily increased, though at the expence of the strength; and the depth may be increased, diminishing however the stability; but there is no ready way in which a a ship, of the present shape, of 41 feet beam can be increased to a breadth of 55 feet —

In the year 1829 the "Constellation" was repaired at an expense (excluding the armament) of 181.000 dollars, of which the rebuilding the Hull was 114.000 dollars; in 1832 the repairs on the hull were 3037 dollars; in 1835 they were 14528 dollars; and in 1840

FIGURE 8a.—Page 1 of official letter from John Lenthall, Naval Constructor, to Commodore Skinner, Chief of Bureau of Construction, Equipment, and Repair, 18 December 1851.

the repairs on the hull alone were, 5.834 dollars — Since that period very little has been done to the ship and it may be safely assumed that she will now require to be entirely rebuilt at a cost but little if any, less than that of a new ship —

If the whole of the materials that enter into the construction of the "Constellation" could be used, it would only amount to about 2/5 of that required for a new ship of the dimensions above given, and it is certain that little or none of it can be used for any such purpose, though probably the lower part of the frame may be sound —

It thus appears to me that the old "Constellation" should be abandond, if it is proposed to build a vessel of 3300 tons to take her place —

If the ancient renown of this ship makes it desirable to retain her (for in point of economy there will be a loss) the plan heretofore under consideration of the Bureau seems well adapted to carrying it out — This ship has been found deficient in stability (though built from the same lines as the Constitution) but in other respects she is well formed —

With a light spar deck and a heavy armament on the gun deck, from an inferior ship of a higher class, she will become the first of a lower class and always be a formidable vessel —

It may be worthy of consideration whether she may not be made into an open deck Corvette, aimed after the

FIGURE 8b.—Page 2 of official letter from John Lenthall, Naval Constructor, to Commodore Skinner, Chief of Bureau of Construction, Equipment, and Repair, 18 December 1851.

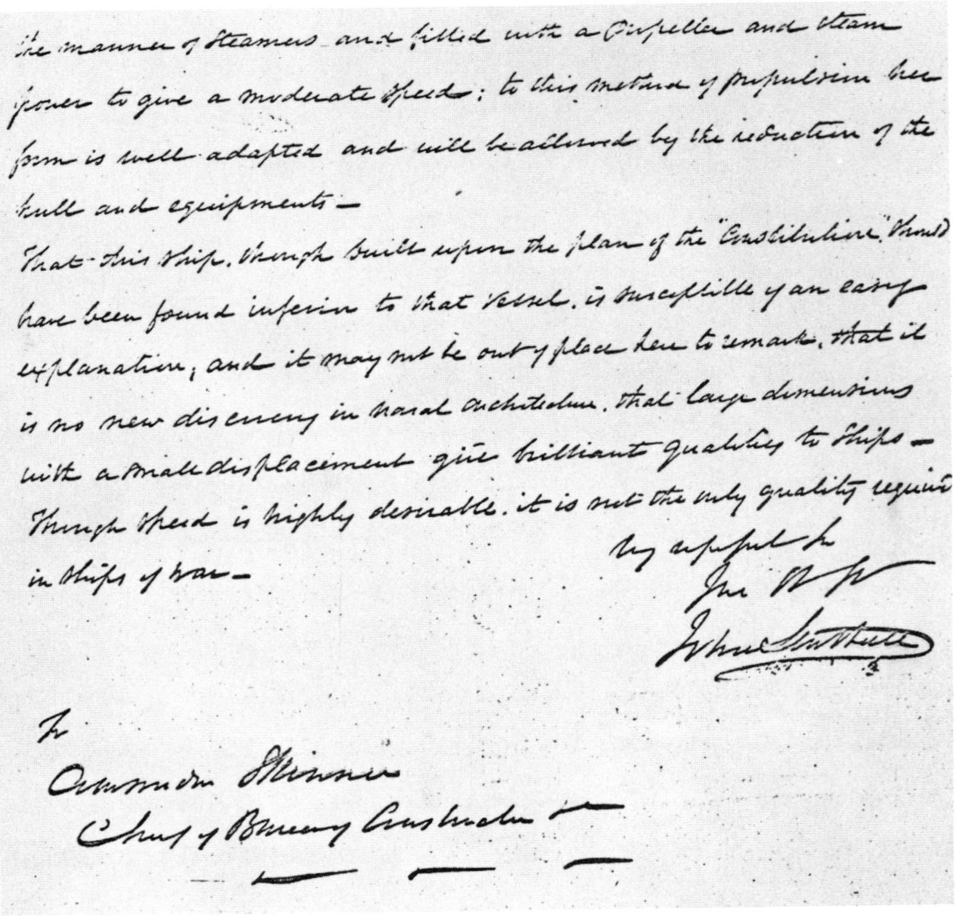
the manner of Steamers and fitted with a Propeller and Steam
power to give a moderate speed; to this method of propulsion her
form is well adapted and will be allowed by the reduction of the
hull and equipments—
That this Ship, though built upon the plan of the "Constitution" should
have been found inferior to that vessel, is susceptible of an easy
explanation; and it may not be out of place here to remark, that it
is no new discovery in naval architecture, that large dimensions
with a small displacement give brilliant qualities to Ships—
Though speed is highly desirable, it is not the only quality required
in Ships of war—
Very respectfully
Your Ob St
John Lenthall

To
Commodore Skinner
Chief of Bureau Construction &c

FIGURE 8c.—Page 3 of official letter from John Lenthall, Naval Constructor, to Commodore Skinner, Chief of Bureau of Construction, Equipment, and Repair, 18 December 1851.

The apparent error in Lenthall's statement that the *Constellation* was built on the lines of the *Constitution* is clarified at the end of this letter.

> That this ship, though built upon the plan of the 'Constitution' should have been found inferior to that vessel is susceptible of an easy explanation; and it may not be out of place here to remark that it is no new discovery in naval architecture that large dimensions with a small displacement give brilliant qualities to ships—Though speed is highly desirable it is not the only quality required in ships of war.

Two things are apparent in this letter. The first is that at the end of 1851 no decision had been reached regarding the end-product of the "rebuilding," secondly, that Lenthall had reservations regarding cobbling up the old frigate, for she was lacking in stability though built as a reduced *Constitution*. Lenthall was dealing with a number of proposals for the "rebuilding" in this letter, stating facts pro and con for each.

The authors' claim (*M.H.M.*, footnote 31, p. 26) now to be considered is: "Since much critical comment directed against the *Constellation* has included statements that in spite of the entire written record of Naval construction during this period, such a subterfuge was practiced on the *Constellation* . . ." (that is, to break up an old ship and replace her with a newly built vessel in the guise of rebuilding). Let the reader consider the record of naval vessels rebuilt listed in Section One and then decide what statements are "in spite of the entire written record of Naval construction in the period."

At the very time the *Constellation*'s future was being worked out, the 74-gun ship-of-the-line *Franklin* was undergoing the "rebuilding" treatment, resulting in the breaking up of the old sailing vessel and the building of a large steam frigate at Portsmouth, New Hampshire, which was not launched until the end of the Civil War, as mentioned in Part 1. She too was built with maintenance funds. Why should the *Constellation* have received different treatment, with the existing precedents?

On page 28 (footnote 33) of the *Maryland Historical Magazine* the authors revert to this subject:

In spite of published statements that the *Constellation* was destroyed in 1852 *sub rosa,* Bureau of Yards and Docks Correspondence January–June 1853 (NA RG 181) contains two letters, January 28 and February 24, 1853 showing that the frigate was not hauled up from the water until February 23rd, 1853, so that work could be commenced on her.

This explains how plans of the hogged keel and of the nine transverse half-sections could be obtained and does not contradict available evidence of the breaking up of the old ship. *The Daily Southern Argus,* Norfolk, Virginia, Monday, July 11, 1853, stated:

The Old Constellation—This old time-honored and time-worn frigate of historical memory has been literally torn to pieces preparatory to the building of a new Constellation. Hundreds of men are employed directly or indirectly upon her massive keel, which has been placed in one of the ship houses. She will be finished with all possible dispatch. The name itself is a source of pride to every American sailor and will no doubt be cherished and esteemed by all lovers of American freedom. Her timbers will be of live oak, every piece of which will be inspected by Mr. Jarvis.

Two new witnesses are now introduced (*M.H.M.*, footnote 34, p. 28), Robert H. Davis and B. F. Delano. Davis is described as having been an apprentice in the Gosport (Norfolk) Navy Yard when the *Constellation* was being worked on, in 1853–55, later becoming a shipwright in the Confederate Navy. Davis is said to have told the story of this work on the *Constellation* to a "Captain W. W. Meade" on 17 September 1904, who then wrote an account of Davis' statements which it is stated is in the "Naval War College Library." Here Davis is said to have died in 1918 and that a "special order" was found, in the "Library," stating the *Constellation*'s flag was to be flown at half-mast, 8 to 10 May 1918.

A very interesting example of "planted" evidence arises with regard to Davis. First, however, "Captain Meade" cannot be readily identified. The only Captain in the U.S. Navy of this name found in the 1905 register was William W. Mead, not Meade, who was Commandant of the navy yard, Portsmouth, New Hampshire, appointed 28 July 1904.

During my investigation at Newport, a "copy" of the "Special Order" for flying the *Constellation's* flag at half-mast was found in the historical files of the Naval Station (Office Services Supervisor, Naval Station, Newport, R.I., File 1 x 20, Constellation Historical Data). See Figure 9. A Xerox facsimile of the "order."

The "order" was typed on relatively new white typewriter paper, without watermark, punched for file staples.

This "document" shows so many errors that it was easily identified as an unauthorized addition and it could be established that it had been recently added to the file. Though dated three days after Davis' death, it does not give the date the flag was to be flown at "half." The creator of this piece of evidence forgot that the authors'

U.S. Naval Training Station
Newport, R.I.

ROUGH to be
PRINTED at Plant

May, 8, 1918

Memo- To. Commanding Officer
U.S.F. Constellation

From- Commanding Officer of the Point

This is authorization to fly the flag at the gaff of the Constellation at half to honor Mr. Charles E. Davis- Born April 13, 1832- Deceased - May 5, 1918.

Whereas Mr. Charles E. David was responsible for the information leading to the peoof that the Constellation was in fact built in Baltimore in the year 1797 and was not a model of 1855.

Whereas Mr. Charles E. Davis worked on the rebuilding of the frigate at the Gosport Navy Yard from 1853- through 1855.

Whereas there is respect for this gentlemen among the existing crew of stated frigate.

Whereas Mr. Davis respected and loved the Constellation as a memorial of our great naval traditions.

Whereas Mr. David visited this ship on every possible occasion.

It shall be deemed fitting that the gaff should fly the flag presented to the ship by Mr. Davis, at half mast, in honor of his deeds and respect for that ship.

FIGURE 9.—Rough draft of memorandum from Commanding Officer of the Point, U.S. Naval Training Station, Newport, R.I., to Commanding Officer, U.S.F. *Constellation*, 8 May 1918.

footnote on Davis said that the "Special Order" found had called for the flag to be half-masted on May 8–10, 1918! Nor did he know how to write such an order, as the "document" shows.

The address is inverted and the use of "Memo" is improper—the source of the

7-1 (Rev. 9-7-60)

REPORT
of the

FBI
LABORATORY

FEDERAL BUREAU OF INVESTIGATION
WASHINGTON, D. C. 20535

To: Mr. Howard I. Chapelle   October 6, 1967
    Senior Historian
    Department of Science and Technology
    Smithsonian Institution
    United States National Museum
    Washington, D. C. 20560

Re: Unknown Subject;
     Typewriting Examination
     Smithsonian Institution   John Edgar Hoover, Director

                                                     YOUR NO.
                                                     FBI FILE NO.
                                                     LAB. NO.   D-545258   AX

Examination requested by: Addressee

Reference: Letter dated September 28, 1967

Examination requested: Document

Specimen:
    Qc1   Xerox copy of a letter dated May 8, 1918, beginning
             "This is authorization to fly the flag..."

Result of examination:

         The typewriting on Qc1 matches Laboratory standards for
    a Royal elite style of type. According to information available
    to the FBI Laboratory, this particular style of type was not
    used prior to June, 1950.

         Qc1 was photographed and is returned herewith.

Enclosure   Registered

FIGURE 10.—Report from the Federal Bureau of Investigation, Washington, D.C., to Howard I. Chapelle, 6 October 1967.

order, or communication, is placed first, the recipient under, in such a Navy communication. The source in this "order" is "Commanding Officer of the Point"—the files show the correct title to have been "Officer in Charge of Point." However, the order to half-mast the flag would be issued by the Commandant of a station. *"U.S.F. Constellation"* was not found in correspondence of the station, *"USS Constellation"* was commonly used; a few instances of *U.S. Frigate Constellation* were found, however.

The "Whereases" are astonishing—the officer commanding the ship is "authorized" to fly "the flag at the gaff" and also "the gaff should fly the flag," as if he would not know where the flag was to be flown without the aid of this "authorization!"

Apparently the "Commanding Officer of the Point" was clairvoyant, for he foresaw F. D. Roosevelt's claim that the corvette was the Baltimore-built frigate by some six months before the Roosevelt brief was written! Since the Roosevelt claim was not published until long after it had been sent to Secretary Daniels, the reference to this matter is additional evidence of the true date of the "document" and of its being a crude attempt to tamper with an official record. The type used in the "special order" is that of a modern manual typewriter, not one of 1918 (Figure 10).

No other document relating to the Davis matter could be found in this file. The original order, of which the "document" is offered as a copy, could not be found of course and the "copy" shows no initials to identify the officers involved.

Another paper found at Newport is a half-sheet of relatively new typewriter paper, without watermark, and not punched for its binder but, rather, forced down over the staples. It has no relationship, that could be discovered, to the rest of the file, 1 x 20 (19) (Constellation Historical Data) and reads as follows:

U.S. Frigate Constellation

Keel laid—1794 [should be 1795]
Stodder's Shipyard—Harris Creek, Baltimore, Md.
Launched Sept. 7, 1797
Designed by—Joshua Humphreys—Philadelphia, Pa. and
David Stodder—Baltimore, Maryland.
Mast Design Thomas Truxtun—Long Island, N.Y. and
David Stodder—Baltimore, Md. [Truxtun's address incorrect]
Changes—Building of 1794–97—Frame spaces from 25 inch to 32 inch—Thin sucked in bow
    from fore-chains to the stem, changed for speed. Completed several inches longer than
    design of Humphreys. Diagonal Riders to stiffen the hull excluded. Length of mast and
    spars changed by the building of Stodder. [sic]

Benjamin F. Delano was a naval constructor stationed at Norfolk in 1852–55 who had been appointed in 1846 from New Hampshire. He retired in 1871, died in 1882. Most of his service was at New York. A man of the same name had a shipyard at Medford, Massachusetts, in the early 1840s. Mr. Roosevelt stated that Delano was a distant relative and that he had a manuscript diary of Delano's for the period of the "rebuilding" of the *Constellation*.

The footnotes in the *Maryland Historical Magazine* article now to be discussed are generally from "Meade's manuscript"; or from "Delano's diary" or journal, neither of which has been produced by the authors but which are represented by Roosevelt's notes "taken from" them according to the authors. Delano is quoted as of March 1852:

Planking from the rail to lower deck removed, together with frames and chain iron [sic] with spar deck [sic] and gun deck removed [May 1853] Old copper composition removed from Constellation hull and piled near the end of the shiphouse. New upper frames are being cut to join the lower while the ship is being cut to pieces [sic] to extend the body [July 1853] new pieces of shoe are being constructed to fit the old keel which is lengthened and still shows sag at both ends. The low parts of the ship are being cottoned [sic] and caulked as they are reusable.

If these statements were accurate and authentic transcripts, something would be very wrong. The United States Navy has always been noted for employing the proper nautical and shipbuilding nomenclature and language in all documents and in conversation; indeed the Navy carries this characteristic to the extreme of calling a floor of a building the deck and the walls bulkheads. It is quite unthinkable that any Naval Constructor would not know, or would not use, the proper language of his profession in his time. How can the Delano entries be justified? Such terms as "chain iron" for chainplates, "upper frames" for top-timbers or futtocks, "cut to pieces" for cut in two, "sag at both ends" for hog or hogged, "low parts" for bottom or underbody and, finally, the use of "cottoned," are impossible to accept as the writing of a competent professional shipbuilder constructor or naval architect (Figure 8). Cotton, by the way, is used for cauking small boats, but oakum was used in large wooden ships, for plank seams and butts. Also the sequence of reported operations is in error, no caulking could or would be done at the described levels of preparation but would be done shortly before coppering and launching. *Constellation* had not been a spar-decked frigate, so far as can be ascertained in naval records.

Next, we have Davis, allegedly a journey-man shipwright at least, trained in a U.S. Navy yard. "Between February and June or July she was stripped down to her berth deck and it was decided that her low decks were good as was her low frames and keel, the old keel was warped [sic], high in the center, low on the ends, she had to have a piece of false keel graved in to straighten out her warped keel and some small pieces fitted in to her old keel."

Again there is the astonishing lack of knowledge of the correct, contemporary nautical and ship building language, by a shipwright in this testimony; "low decks" for decks—the berth deck would be the lowest deck in this ship—"low frames" for floors and lower futtocks, "warped" keel for hogged keel. The shoe or false keel would not be "graved in" for it ran the full length of the keel, so would have been fitted.

The Admiral Capps' report, *Major Battle Damage* mentioned earlier also shows unprofessional language "New materials, timbers and exterior hull . . . from the keel upward, False keel, ¼ of the keel, keelson and members, 15 foot inch splice [24] in stem all new outside plank from the 15 foot line and to the rail ⅕ oak planking below the 15 foot line at lengthened area." This is certainly not a report on repairs, by a trained shipwright, on the *Constellation*. Incidentally, Admiral Capps discussed Roosevelt's *Our First Frigates* before the Society of Naval Architects and Marine Engineers in 1914 [25] and did not mention having reported on *Constellation,* which would be pertinent in a discussion of the paper. The Capps report will be examined more fully, when the Polland paper is discussed.

In the examination of the Roosevelt brief (p. 21), comment was withheld on statements regarding the surprise when it was "discovered" that the *Constellation* had not been built to the official draught, after hauling her out at Norfolk in 1853. Footnotes describing this (pp. 29–30, footnotes 35 to 39 inclusive, *M.H.M.*) follow.

Delano diary, January 1853 "in pencil"—"Underwater body of Constellation does not match drawing of Humphrey plan or the sketched drawings 1852 showing sections of the hull. This fact was discovered during the docking of the ship to fit her to the blocking to draw her into the ship house."

Davis' testimony "I will never forget the mess when it was discovered that this ship did not compare to the plans of her drawn in 1794 in Philadelphia. Someone was wrong, either they did not follow the plans or they built her from some other plans, she had to have all of her ballast piled while draftsmen lifted the lines of her underwater from her hull." The authors further state that—

"The sections referred to in the Delano quotation are undoubtedly those of NA plan C&R 107–13–4B (Transverse Sections of Frigate Constellation, Feb. 1853) which shows nine sections of the hull of the Humphreys design."

These statements, in the Roosevelt brief and in the supporting footnotes again show lack of knowledge of shipbuilding and shipyard practices and of nomenclature that is apparent throughout the *Maryland Historical Magazine* article. Contrary to Roosevelt's description of the preliminary steps in rebuilding the *Constellation,* a vessel was not hauled "up the blocks," she would be hauled on the ways and supported by skids or sliding ways (as has been stated in Section Two), if hauled into a ship-house.

Delano's "diary" refers to "sketched drawings, 1852" which the authors rightly identify as *Transverse Sections of Frigate Constellation Feb. 1853* though "Delano" dates them *1852*. Davis is quoted to the effect that the *Constellation* had to have all of her ballast piled (ashore) so the draftsmen could take off her lines, which was not correct. In an old wooden sailing ship the ballast would usually be removed before hauling, not only to prevent straining the hull but also to reduce the load in hauling. Taking-off could be done without reference to the ballast in any case. It is impossible to believe that a Navy Yard-trained shipwright would use such terms as to "take the lines of her underwater from her hull," for such a trained man would say "take off her lines," of course.

The most curious claim develops in the Roosevelt brief and in the authors statements; that the ship was discovered not to have been built on the official draught when hauling in 1853. If this had been true, the United States Navy would have employed an important vessel for 56 years (from 1797 to 1853) whose hull-form was unknown to the construction authorities! It might be argued that in heaving-down for repairs of the hull, this would not be apparent, but this is not really true. However, the Norfolk Navy Yard had a drydock in service after 1833, or for 20 years before the hauling in 1853 that is being discussed. In this period the *Constellation* must have been docked a number of times. It would be interesting to know how this could be done without making the discovery that surprised the Norfolk Yard in 1853.

Comments on the 1966 Polland Paper[26]

M R. POLLAND'S PAPER is, mainly, an explanation of his design for the reconstruction of the existing corvette *Constellation* as a frigate. Only a portion of the paper refers to the matters being discussed. The author states, however, that extensive research was carried on, naming various places where source material was apparently found, including the "Naval War College Library" and "Naval Training Station Museum," Newport, Rhode Island (previously burned according to the 1961 M.H.M. article). The result is much repetition of the *Maryland Historical Magazine* article claims and liberal use of "Naval War College Library" "documentation."

In his introduction to his paper (page II), Polland refers to Franklin D. Roosevelt's paper "Our First Frigates," but fails to note that Roosevelt had not then formulated his claim that a substitution had been made for the official draught of *Constellation*. The claim is repeated, concerning the loss of the "Theodore Roosevelt Collection" of plans, documents, etc., when the "Newport Naval Training Station Museum" burned. The continued uncertainty regarding the location of the "Theodore Roosevelt Collection" is difficult to understand, in the light of the extensive research that was said to have been done by the Baltimore group.

The Introduction of the Polland paper repeats the claim that the corvette is the old frigate, altered in 1853–55. In his preliminary remarks (p. 2) Mr. Polland makes it clear that the Baltimore Committees (there were at least two) decided, before starting research, that it was their objective to prove the Roosevelt claims to be correct, not to weigh the evidence pro and con. It was recognized, however, that the corvette had no resemblance to the official draught of the frigate *Constellation*. This made it necessary that evidence be produced to impeach the Congressional papers, published in *American State Papers,* vol. 1, and also the accumulation of plans, offsets, and technical material in the records of the U.S. Navy's Bureau of Construction and Repair and of its predecessor, the Bureau of Equipment, Construction and Repair, and contemporary documents in the Fox papers, and in the Humphrey papers as well.

It is admitted by Polland (p. 3) that the corvette was obviously "represented" in John Lenthall's plan dated 1853, and, it might have been added, the corvette was built on the offsets: "Dimensions of the Spar deck Sloop of War Constellation taken from the Mould loft Floor" (National Archives, C&R, 142–1–7 "Constellation" 1853). This, had the Committees examined it, was a complete lofting record, giving offsets

43

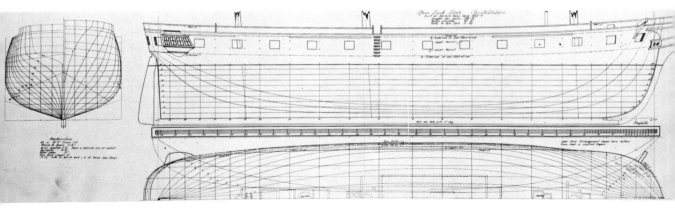

FIGURE 11.—Draught of corvette *Constellation,* 1853, drawn from Lenthall draught and offsets.

for proof that the corvette was built entirely from Lenthall's lines, now in the National Archives (C&R 28–3–5) dated "June 1853 Scale 5 feet=1 inch." A body plan of this design is in the Lenthall collection, titled "Spar Deck Sloop of War Constellation," John Lenthall, scale 5 feet=1 inch, in ink, with "New Constellation" written above the title in pencil.

The Committee overlooked other information that is contained in these offsets, which show that they had been corrected, as to heights, in sheer to allow for the "hang" of the keel, amounting to three inches. This contradicts Roosevelt's claim that the original keel hog was built into the "new" ship by retaining the old frigate's bottom. "Hang" is reverse of hog and the "sag" is at midsection, not in the ends. Hang was employed in wooden hulls over 100 feet long to prevent hog from appearing after the vessel had been launched, when strain is first brought on the structural longitudinals in which, in a wooden ship, some movement usually takes place. This was recommended practice in American Bureau rules for wooden ship construction, as a matter of fact, until large wooden ships ceased to be built in the present century.

There is no evidence whatsoever that the Lenthall draught and the offsets of 1853 were take-offs of any old vessel; rather, a new design is obviously shown. The offset table is not the very limited measurements that would be "taken from the work" in the cobbling-up of an old frigate, as described by Roosevelt, to produce the corvette in which the old keel and practically the whole bottom of the old frigate are said to have been retained.

The Committee ran into some remarkable material. In the spring of 1960 they found a portion of an inboard plan of the *Constellation* (corvette) in the F. D. Roosevelt Library on which a vertical line had been drawn at frame F., labeled *"New 12 ft. aft."* and initialed F.D.R. This is apparently supposed to be evidence, but merely shows the ignorance of the person who drew the vertical line. Station F is well forward of ⊕ on Lenthall's draught and the cutting-in-two, as claimed by Roosevelt and the Committee, would have had to have been made at ⊕ (dead flat station) in order to fair the "insert"—12 feet long—into the two halves of the hull.

The Fox "Sworn statement" is quoted (Polland, p. 13) and the claim that Humphreys had no experience in building a man-of-war is repeated here. Much time and effort would have been avoided if the Committee had studied the history of American naval shipbuilding before committing themselves to unsupported claims. The Committee's lack of knowledge in this area led to an attempt to build up Stodder's reputation as a great shipbuilder and authority. They state (Polland, p. 14), with regard to the omission of the diagonal riders in the *Constellation:* "Undoubtedly Stodder fully concurred with Truxtun on the deletion of the diagonal riders. His own experience was by this time well known and more than a little respected in Washington" (the capital was then Philadelphia). This statement is referenced from the "Naval War College Library," "Pickering to Stodder letter of May 18, 1795." (In his biography of Truxtun [27] Eugene S. Ferguson gives an indication of Stodder's reputation.) In regard to an article in the *Maryland Journal* that embarrassed him (and which he suspected was sponsored by Stodder), Truxtun wrote Fox that it might be "some of Stodder's nonsense" [sic]. No indication has been found that Stodder was more than a practical merchant-ship builder of no marked distinction. His complaints about *Constellation* may be summarized as—she is built too expensively (which undoubtedly was true, as is still often the case with government vessels).

Some comments in Mr. Pollands' paper (p. 17) show that he, too, though a naval architect, was unacquainted with wooden shipbuilding: "Allowing for later repairs, such as that of 1888 and including work performed in 1904, there still remained those most important *hand hewn timbers* which at this point were considered to (at the least) pre-date the 1853 reconstruction." This implies that hand-hewn timbers were an acceptable evidence of great age. A visit to some of the boatyards in Maine and Maryland today would show the adze and the broad axe are still tools in use for shaping heavy timbers, dubbing sawn frames, and other work on a large wooden hull.

A rather curious statement (p. 17) is that the old *Constellation* rolled excessively and that this could be counteracted by a reduction in tumble home, which was done in 1812 under the supervision of "Constructor Captain Tingey." As the tumble home, in the American frigates whose plans exist, was quite small at main or gun deck level and marked only as the main rail was approached, the amount of tumble home therefore had no marked effect on either rolling or initial stability and would not have effect until some condition produced extreme heel. When the angle of heel reached the point where the lee side of the gun deck was at water level the guns were hanging on their breechings and tackles. Hence the frigates were sailed at less than 15 degrees of heel so far as possible. It is also stated here that *Constellation* was one of the fastest ships afloat. This would be a very difficult matter to prove. The rank of "Constructor Captain" was never established in the U.S. Navy and Tingey had no claim to be a Constructor.

It is further stated (p. 17): "Also to be considered is the fact that the lower shrouds were continually rubbing on the bulwark rails causing excessive strains and obvious stretching and chaffing damaged to the shrouds." Our shipbuilding ancestors were not so stupid as to allow this. The channels were made wide enough so that the shrouds or lanyards were at least 4 inches outboard of the rail when set up.

Another version of the Tingey report of 1812–13 is given (p. 18): "To remove

DEPARTMENT OF THE NAVY

Office of the Chief of Naval Operations

Washington 25, D.C.

Op-29/pam
Ser 11P29
5 Jan 1954

From: Chief of Naval Operations
To: Commandants of Naval Districts and Commanders of Naval Ship-
       yards

Subj: History of USS CONSTELLATION; clarification of

1. The Navy Department has approved the proposals contained in a bill pending before the Congress which would authorize the Bureau of Ships to dismantle and scrap the USS CONSTELLATION. The introduction of this bill has heightened interest in the CONSTELLATION and her history and has led to some newspaper statements which have questioned whether or not the CONSTELLATION is the "original frigate."

2. As early as 1811 the expense of repairing the CONSTELLATION was estimated at $120,000 (SECNAV ltr to Congressional Committee), the original cost having been $314,212.15. An inspection in 1818 found the hull defective in many places, while in 1828 the outside planking of the ship from the rail to the water's edge was found to be in a state of decay. Extensive repairs are known to have been made in 1812, 1828–29, 1832, 1834–35, and 1838–39, before the 1853 rebuilding. The materials used in making these repairs included at least 18,121 cubic feet of timber and 514,601 square feet of planking.

3. In a letter dated December 26, 1851, from the Commandant Gosport (Norfolk) Naval Shipyard to SECNAV, we find:

> "In submitting to the Department the proposition to repair and *remodel* the frigate Constellation I had in view your recommendation 'to build every year two vessels, in order that the Navy may keep pace with the improvements of the age—'
>
> "Believing that it required a special act of Congress to authorize this very desirable measure, and much doubting whether that body would act upon the recommendation during its present Session. I ventured to Suggest a mode by which I thought these difficulties might be remedied, and the work commenced."

FIGURE 12a.—Page 1 of official letter from Chief of Naval Operations, 5 January 1954, concerning the history of the *Constellation*.

4. The Secretary of the Navy, the Hon. J. C. Dobbin, in his annual report for 1853, records that the CONSTELLATION was in the process of being converted to a first-class sloop-of-war. In 1854, SECNAV reported further:

> ". . . the Constellation, was built in 1797, as a frigate of the second class, and had been many times rebuilt. Being found altogether unworthy of further repairs, she has been rebuilt as a spar-deck sloop . . ."

5. Mr. Howard I. Chappelle in his book, *The History of the American Sailing Navy*, published by W. W. Norton & Co., New York, 1949, correctly states that the CONSTELLATION was rebuilt in 1853–54, and that her original design was changed from a frigate to a sloop-of-war or corvette.

6. The following dimensions of the CONSTELLATION's hull are pertinent:

	1797	*1854*
Length between perpendiculars	164'0"	176'0"
Beam moulded	40'6"	41'0"
Depth, in hold	13'6"	21'1"

The CONSTELLATION of 1797 was rated as a 36-gun frigate, and her displacement was recorded as 1,278 tons. SECNAV report for 1854 describes her as a 22-gun sloop-of-war. (CONSTITUTION was a 44-gun frigate of 1,576 tons.)

7. It will be apparent from the facts set forth above that there was such an extensive rebuilding in 1852–53 that there are grounds for stating that the present ship dates from that period. Probably there are very few, if any, timbers of 1797 in the present vessel. On the other hand, there are very few timbers in the present day CONSTITUTION which date back to her first commissioning, although her hull lines and original dimensions have been preserved. If any restoration of the CONSTELLATION were to be attempted the logical course would be to rebuild the frigate of 1797, from the keel up. The original frigate had a history well worthy of preservation.

8. In spite of all the facts recorded above, some persons contend that the present CONSTELLATION, as the direct inheritor of the old traditions, is, in spirit at least, the original one. Major General Jim Dan Hill, now the Commanding General of the 32nd Infantry Division, Wisconsin National Guard, President of Wisconsin State College, in Superior, author of *The History of the Texas Navy*, and *Sea Dogs of the Sixties*, who believes that the name of the CONSTELLATION should be given to a new aircraft carrier, had this to say in a recent article about the frigates UNITED STATES, CONSTITUTION, and CONSTELLATION:

FIGURE 12b.—Page 2 of official letter from Chief of Naval Operations, 5 January 1954, concerning the history of the *Constellation*.

"Of course, all three ships [as of 1860] had long since been repaired so often they were like the bowie knife that Cactus Pete Dabney's great great grandfather carried through the Battle of San Jacinto, and with which no one knows how many Indians had been scalped.

"I had hefted the knife and said: 'Pete, you and your ancestors have been operating with mighty dull cutlery, or by now the blade would be honed to the size of a toothpick.'

" 'That knife,' he retorted, 'has had three new blades, complete through the grips, two new guards, five new bone grips held in place by nine new sets of cross rivets; but take my word for it, that weapon is the same identical bowie knife my old great great grandpappy carried at San Jacinto.' "

[signed]   JOHN B. HEFFERNAN
             By direction

Note: This letter is issued so that questions of fact about the CONSTELLA-TION can be answered locally.

FIGURE 12c.—Page 3 of official letter from Chief of Naval Operations, 5 January 1954, concerning the history of the *Constellation*.

excess tumble in the home come of the ship—new second and third futtocks from the bow to the stern. To renew rot in timbers and to *give the ship seven inches more oak from all wales on both hull sides,* etc., etc. . . . . Tingey, Capt." This says in effect that the entire frame of the ship, outboard of the floors and the first futtocks to the bilge, was replaced, *for the futtocks were numbered from the floors to the main or upper deck in wooden shipbuilding!* Tingey hardly intended to "renew rot" in timbers. The great alteration seems actually to have been the addition of 7 inches of oak plank over the wales, thus increasing the extreme beam 14 inches. The reputation of the frigate for lack of stiffness or initial stability was not changed by Tingey repairs for, as we have seen, in his letter of 1851, Lenthall mentions her lack of stability as an objection to the vessel. "Home come" is not found in any nautical vocabulary known to this critic.

Mr. Polland (p. 20) attempts to show that the *Constellation* was given a round stern prior to 1851 and refers to a plan "used for a survey of the mizzen mast." This is said to be in National Archives "RG–45," but the Archives staff have not been able to find it, with only this available reference. The date of the plan is stated to be 1829 but the survey it shows is said to be dated 1840. The author does not attempt to explain this except by inference, on the grounds of possible convenience to the draughtsman in reworking part of an old plan. The "1829" date is tied to the "destroyed" Samuel Humphreys statement in 1829 in the "Naval War College Library," a convenient, but not necessarily accurate procedure. However, this eliminated the square transom of the old frigate and gave an apparently plausible explanation for the round stern of the corvette as part of the old vessel.

The relation of "moulded beam" to "extreme beam" seems to have given trouble, but some of this seems to be due to the need of reconciling the 40-foot moulded beam of the frigate with the 41-foot moulded beam of the corvette. The Roosevelt procedure of rebuilding would not have produced such an increase, nor would the Committee's version of the 1853–55 rebuilding process.

A most interesting "document" is presented by Mr. Polland on pp. 32–41 of his paper. It is titled "The Major Battle Damage, Repairs and Reconstruction to the U.S. Ship 'CONSTELLATION' 1797–1855, Prepared by the Bureau of Construction and Repair—USN, by Rear Admiral Washington L. Capps, Chief of the Bureau, at the direction of Hon. Truman H. Newberry, Assistant Secretary, Department of the Navy, FILE #–1231–A." This, it will be recalled, is one of the "documents" from the "Navy War College Library" that has already been mentioned in two short citations. We now have, apparently, the full, alleged document-transcript. Unaccountable nautical and shipbuilding phrases appear throughout this manuscript. First there is: "Designed—Joshua Humphreys—Note—Humphreys' design was a model to follow but changes were made by the various constructors building the United States, Constitution, and Constellation" (Polland, p. 32). Then follows, in a reference to *American State Papers,* vol. 1, pp. 13–16: "Full dimensions in file 1208–s, which also contains data on materials, stores, specifications for interest only as these were generally not followed." This citation is next followed by "Note: Major Stodder worked from a model built in his yard, 1795 and it is very doubtful if Humphreys plans were followed except in the sizes of material." "File 1208–s" cannot be accounted for; it has no reference to *American State Papers.* No proof is offered that the specifications in the *American State Papers* were not followed.

In view of what has been examined earlier, the so-called Capps' report is as questionable as its "source." There has been no evidence produced that Stodder "worked from a model built at his yard, 1795"; the inaccuracy of this claim has been shown earlier, for no record of a model exists. The repetition of the fiction that Stodder clandestinely substituted his design for the authorized draught of 1794 in so many impossible methods or situations is now supplemented by the inference that Stodder built from a model, instead of the authorized draught, in his yard, openly, in spite of Truxtun's presence! Though Humphreys visited the *Constellation* at launching, he apparently did not comment on any change in form or design, for there is nothing of this sort in his papers, and, to emphasize the point, nothing can be found in the Fox papers at Salem, Massachusetts, or others that are known, showing any knowledge by these men of a departure from the authorized hull design, by Stodder or anyone else. Indifference to unauthorized departure from their design does not fit the characters of Humphreys and Fox, as revealed in their papers.

It may be repetitious to examine the Capps' report further, but having stated that the "documents" cited by Mr. Polland will be examined, it is necessary to continue. Under the heading "Battle–Damage" (Polland, p. 33), the curious nautical and shipbuilding nomenclature that has marked the Roosevelt and committee citations is even more extensive; for example, under "Spar-Deck", "hatch rising on two sides" is given for coamings and "transom facing" for, apparently, transom planking.

Also "four 3rd futtocks" are "spliced," rather than scarphed or replaced, with 14 more 3rd futtocks listed. (Futtocks were usually "butted" and not scarphed, by the way.) As will be seen, replacement of lower futtocks was a common repair in the Capps' report. (The reader will remember that they are numbered from the keel upward.) Why the ship required so much repair below the bilge (which normally outlives the topsides in a wooden hull) and so little in the topsides is not stated. On the Berth-Deck both "sheathing" and "ceiling" are described as "spliced." What sheathing is meant cannot be determined, but all sheathing was butted, as in most other planking. Normally "sheathing" is plank on the inside of the bulwarks or is thick plank laid over bottom plank, while "ceiling" is the plank on the inboard face of the frames. Finally, it is stated that she was "Not Hulled" and was not damaged below the water! This makes the replacement of 3rd futtocks, listed as battle damage, utterly incomprehensible.

In the report of the frigate's damages in its second action (Polland, p. 34), under "Masts and Rigging," "sailyard" is listed as part of the spars attached to the bowsprit. No such spar name can be found in marine dictionaries. Under "Trim" is listed— repairs to "⅓ of the port quartergallery." "Trim" is used in this reference to mean decorative parts, which is incorrect. As an estimate this would do, but hardly as a report on a repair. In repairs, fractional quantities are employed only in areas, in estimating, as "¼ of deck to be recaulked," and not to bulwark or gallery repairs. Next (Polland, p. 35) it is stated that the *Constellation* was "Hauled" in the Washington Navy Yard, January 1812, whereas Tingey is represented as writing to Stewart that she had been "careened", or hovedown, for repairs (Polland, p. 18). The Washington yard had neither drydock nor marine railway at this time.[28] Tingey is called "Constructor-Captain" again (p. 35)— this time by a Chief of the Bureau of Construction and Repair! Among the oddities in marine terminology are "all bow assembly-[a very modern term applied to construction, not used in 1812] sprit and booms." In this report the "Second futtocks" were all replaced! "all plank with wales above the 12 foot line" is apparently intended to mean the whole topside planking. Apparently this frigate had 36 lodging and dagger knees below the *berth deck;* unusual to say the least for such knees were commonly placed on the main or gun deck only. Under "Exterior Hull", "chain ports" for chain hawse, "chain iron" for chain plates, and a strange sequence: "hull caulked, treenailed, and coppered." Chain cable were not issued in the Navy until after 1813, by the way.

Next, another questionable statement (p. 36) is that in 1828 the "Construction and Repair Department" (nonexistent in 1828) stated "The Constellation was different from other frigates of the class in that she had a fore-castle and quarterdeck–fore and aft with *platforms running from fore to aft for marines* and with just enough room to work the carronades and *for their coil* [sic]" (italics mine). The only frigates of her "class" then afloat in the U.S. Navy and serviceable were *Congress* and, perhaps, the British *Macedonian.* Both had quarterdeck and forecastle connected by *gangways,* as was usual in frigates of all nations. So far as can now be determined, the forecastle and quarterdeck, connected by gangways, were never altered in these two frigates; but *Congress* 2nd was built with a spardeck instead. The frigates authorized in 1794 were large enough, however, to have wide gangways on which carronades were mounted, but this strained the ships and soon the gangway batteries were removed. It should be noted that the report uses "platforms" for gangways, "coil" for recoil, and elsewhere "grates" for hatch gratings and "hatch boards" for hatch covers. The ship had continuous bottom repairs, according to the Capps' report, for in 1829 she had, in addition to "213 new timbers and stanchions", "27 first futtocks, 53 second futtocks, and 68 third futtocks all new". On the "Spar-Deck" something called a "bowsprit hook" and, surprisingly, new "mast holes," are listed among the repairs! She also had new "fore and mainsail sheet bitts" (Polland, p. 37) and "15 feet of stem, cutwater and heads," "10 fore-hooks under keel, coppered and after calking [sic] inside and out." It is to be feared the "transcriber" or author went adrift, for a good part of the "transcript" makes no sense. What "fore and mainsail sheet bitts" were on a square-rigged ship is a mystery.

The repairs of 1832 (p. 37) show she had a "snow-mast" instead of a properly named trysail mast or spencer-mast, all new plank to "anchor ports," whatever these were, and was fitted with something called "two messangers [sic] to the main topsaid [sic] sheet bitts." Since messengers were cordage that did not lead to bitts, identification is impossible. Another innovation also appears: "quarter-piece on starboard hull, scuppered leaded together with plank sheer coppered." It would be interesting to know what this repair was intended to be and why the planksheer should be coppered—if this "transcript" were authentic. The ignorance of proper terms used in wooden ship-building displayed in the alleged Capps' report makes it impossible to take this "document" seriously, even if it could not be otherwise established that its source is wholly imaginary.

The repairs of 1835 mention "longcombing" on main hatch, "new platforms [for gangways] running fore and aft for marines"; the capstan is "scarphed," "new cross cable" and "cross bitt" are fitted. Why and where a capstan would be scarphed, and what "cross cables" were, are additional mysteries. "Hogging of the keel filled with form [sic] [?] and lead and a false keel attached with the entire hull re-coppered including the keel and false keel after the ship was completely caulked." This is the way it stands in Polland's paper at any rate: a collection of errors in nautical nomenclature (Polland, p. 38).

According to this document the *Constellation* was at the Norfolk yard from 1845 to 1852, hauled 26 February 1853. There is no need to examine this part of the report in much detail but it is useful to mention a few more oddities: "bottom cottoned and caulked," a "new offiers [sic] quarterwalk across the deck" (Polland, p. 39). Also "bow yoke and hook" (p. 40) are mentioned. The "quarterwalk across the deck" cannot be identified nor "bow yoke and hook," though possibly breast hook may have been intended; "mast sockets" and "hold walks" (p. 40)—"mast sockets" are presumably mast steps, but what "hold walks" might be is impossible to say.

It is needless to discuss most of Mr. Polland's statements in his Summary (pp. 93–98) for they repeat matter that has been examined in the Roosevelt Brief discussion (pages 17–22). The remainder (Polland, pp. 96–97) can quickly be disposed of: an "Inspector's Report January 1854," found in the Franklin D. Roosevelt Library "Group 10, Naval Affairs, Hyde Park, N.Y.," which is transcribed to read "the counter rounded and the new guns delivered . . . the iron work has been cleaned and painted and will be refitted on the ship and masting. . . ." Why the "inspector" should report

FIGURE 13.—Corvette *Constellation,* showing round stern.

"the counter rounded" when the round-stern was an integral part of the ship's structure that, according to the committee's claim, had been added long before 1853, is unexplainable.

The next "document" (Polland, p. 97) is represented to be the whole report of Tingey, at Washington, in "December-1811." This is the "Naval War College Library" document mentioned in footnote 24, p. 24, *M.H.M.* It reads:

In January 1812 the ship was brought up to the dock and was found to be in fair condition but not in condition to be an active man-of-war and suitable to engage a British ship of equal size of arms. She had excessive tumble-home due to the excessive curve from the widest beam to the bulwark rail. Truxtun and Murray had tried to remedy this by replacing bulwarks in a more upright position, but this had come in way of the standing rigging and through the working of the vessel had cut the shrouds through on more than one occasion. The excessive tumble-home had also meant the death of a few men who had climbed outboard of the gun deck to ram home or load in the heat of battle. These unfortunate souls had been swept over when the ship came about sharply or in several instances were surprised by the firing of a carronade from above and lost their balance, being lost at sea during engagements when there was no time to pick them up.

The ship has a strange feature in that she is very sharp forward and this probably accounts for her great speed—some of which is lost by the flat transom that runs from starboard to larboard and from the taffrail under water to the post.

Brig Adaline—water ways and top timber on the main deck much strained & open breast hook over the bowsprit started bowsprit beam sprung fore topmast cap damaged cathead on the starboard bow and plankshire sprung and split & broken, trestle trees and crosstrees broken & split, flying jib boom gone fore boom and gaff sprung. bulwark on starboard side quarter split and damaged, mast hoops mostly gone, fore topsail and fore yard sprung and rendered unfit for service, starboard swifter chafed mostly off fore and main peak downhaul gone top mast and flying jib stays chafed and spauled, gammoning of bowsprit gone. lifts gone top said sheets & tyes much injured. throat halyard block gone, starboard top mast backstay dead eye and chain gone clue of the jib gone & jib sheet, sprit and fore topsail split main and fore sail cut and blown to pieces. square sail cut and blown away, rigging of jib boom all gone . . . lanyards to the fore shrouds chafed and spauled no long boat nor gally . . . . to repair we recommend the waterways, timberheads and top timber on the main deck to be recaulked and breast hook over the bowsprit bolted, bowsprit beam secured with a thick clamp bolted on the forward side fore top to be repaired & cap to be hooped. New cathead and plankshire on starboard side, new trestle and crosstrees, new flying jibboom, fore boom & gaff, swifter on starboard side new, bulkwards repaired. Fore & main peak & downhaul topmast and flying jib. gammoning of bowsprit to be replaced new throat halyard block, top mast dead eye strap & chain replaced. clew of the jib in fore topsail to be repaired, new main, fore & square sail. Rigging for the jib room . . . lanyards to be replaced with new long boat, galley & cooking stove to be replaced with new, remnant of main, fore sail & rigging & spars to be sold. 4 Sept. 1837.

FIGURE 14.—Example of shipbuilding survey reports for repairs of Maine vessels, using proper shipbuilding nomenclature, 1836–1837. Punctuation and spelling as in original. (Courtesy of William A. Baker, N.A.)

The hull planking of the ship is very thin especially in the wales and in the thickness of the port coverings. There are no quaker guns aboard and when a gun is out of position for any reason there being no substitute to fill the opening which could bring on engagement from the less equal hull in battle.

The wound-work on the masts should be renew'd and in their sted [sic]-iron should be used to provide im-movabl' strength for masts and booms.

The boats aboard could hardly be called sea-worthy and if all were lost [sic] they would probably take many poor souls to a watery grave due to leakage and rot. It was reported by the last Captain that two guns burst on the voyage from the Barbary Coast to this yard and that those being old carronades bored for 24 but worn to perhaps 26 pounds [sic].

The interior is shameful and this is not due to the command of the last Captain, as his books lead me to believe Barron is at fault and he should be responsible for the repairs needed by this ship. Tingey Washington-*December–1811*" [italics mine].

Parts of this "document" were examined earlier (p. 33) but the whole "report" adds to the humor of the Roosevelt brief and the authors' documentation. The "document" is dated December 1811 (in the "NWCL papers" the day of writing is commonly omitted) but describes the condition of the ship in *1812*! It gives a most fantastic description of the effect of the "excessive" tumble home and of the attempts to correct it by the vessel's captains, who are presumed to have practically rebuilt the ship's topsides while in commission! The description of men loading outside the gunports does not suggest how they obtained foothold there, so that they could be swept away in tacking. This would also mean that the frigate then heeled enough to bring the men into the water, if they were perched outboard, so she must have taken in water through the open ports on every tack! I wonder if anyone has seen any reference to an issue of quaker guns to U.S. Navy vessels? "Thin plank at wales" would mean the bottom plank was even thinner, for the wales were the thickest planks outboard. The lack of *quaker guns* was certainly lamentable, since the ports could not be filled; this would lead, if the reasons given can be interpreted, to the enemy attacking the weaker side of the frigate! The strange use of "hull" to mean side, "starboard hull" for starboard side, is another of the errors that appear in this report.

In the Bibliography of the paper (p. 112) a letter of Delano to "Harte," Chief of the Bureau of Construction and Repair, 27 February 1853, is quoted. Delano knew the chief well and his name was Hartt.

The paper contains a "Glossary of Terms Used Herein," but unfortunately does not contain any of the terminology in question, either in the Roosevelt brief or in the supporting documentation.

It will be asked why so much emphasis has been placed on the use of the incorrect or unprofessional, even humorous, nautical terminology and language that is so extensively shown in the Roosevelt brief and in its supporting documentation. The answer is that the authors chose to employ what obviously are intended to appear as "official reports" of competent, professional men concerning the technical matters involved. Therefore, in evaluating these, it is very desirable to establish the validity of the authorship given for each "report." If these, upon examination, appear not to have been written in professional nautical language, but instead show extensive ignorance of the proper nomenclature and terminology of sailing ships and of wooden shipbuilding, then the "reports" are discredited. But it is necessary to show that the impeachment is not based on chance errors growing out of haste, carelessness, or mistakes in transcribing the reports. And to do this, it is necessary to show a large number of examples, particularly the most glaringly incorrect nomenclature that was used.

Tingey, Truxtun, and Capps have been cited, in the footnotes of the brief, as sources for reports and statements that exhibit an almost complete ignorance of technical terms that would be known to the most junior officer in their times. Delano, the experienced naval constructor, is credited with an ignorance of the terminology of his profession that would have shamed the newest apprentice in his age.

Shipbuilding nomenclature in the days of sailing ships was more extensive than today, when a great deal of the special nomenclature of the past is no longer needed. However, the peculiar shipbuilding and nautical nomenclature of the period of sail has been preserved in old works on naval architecture and shipbuilding, as well as in old books on seamanship. There are, also, old and new marine dictionaries that supplement the technical books. Altogether, these sources give a very complete vocabulary of shipbuilding and nautical terms that would be used by officers of the Navy, naval constructors, and shipwrights in the periods under discussion.

It must now be apparent that "The Theodore Roosevelt Collection" of *Constellation* documents, etc., can be impeached. This can be done not only by investigating the claimed locations of the collection and the obvious impossibility of verifying its existence but also by examining the alleged extracts or "transcripts," which have been published by the *Constellation* Committees, showing an almost complete ignorance of shipbuilding and naval terminology and nomenclature.

Yet, on the very flimsy evidence that has been used to support the *Constellation* claims, a grossly inaccurate "history" of the ship has been created and imposed upon what must be a naive public. This has led to heavy expenditures of public and private funds that cannot be justified on any "historical" basis.

The corvette *Constellation* is of historical interest as the last sailing man-of-war, designed and built as such by the United States Navy in 1853–55 at Norfolk, Virginia. Therefore, her restoration should be as the corvette shown in the C&R plans of this ship, not as the Baltimore frigate of 1797, or as a frigate of any other date. In any attempt to create a frigate, out of this corvette, a historical ship will be destroyed to produce a monstrously inaccurate "reconstruction."

NOTES

[1] CHARLES SCARLETT, JR., and others, "Yankee Race Horse: The U.S.S. *Constellation,*" *Maryland Historical Magazine* (March 1961), vol. 56, no. 1, pp. 15–31. Hereinafter referred to as M.H.M.

[2] LEON D. POLLAND, *The Frigate "Constellation": An Outline of the Present Restoration* (Society of Naval Architects and Marine Engineers, 1966).

[3] The chronological history of the building of the Constellation at Baltimore and description of the building organization is taken from *American State Papers, Documents, Legislative and Executive of Congress of the United States, from the First Session of the First to the Second Session of the 18th Congress inclusive, commencing March 3, 1789, and ending March 5, 1825* (Washington, 1834), vol. 1: Naval Affairs.

[4] Plan in Vice-Admiral PARIS, *Souvenirs de Marine, Collection de Plans ou Dessins de Navires et de Bateaux Anciens ou Modernes, Existants on Disparus avec les Elements numeriques Necessaire à Construction* (Paris, 1892), vol. V, plate 277: *L'Indien.* See also HOWARD I. CHAPELLE, *The History of the American Sailing Navy* (New York: W. W. Norton & Company, Inc.), plate IV.

[5] *American State Papers,* vol. 1.

[6] *American State Papers,* vol. 1. The progress reports, according to this source, were not made at regular intervals.

[7] *American State Papers,* vol. 1. Probably due to the delays in construction, the progress reports became more numerous in 1797.

[8] Records of the Bureau of Construction and Repair, U.S. Navy (National Archives, Washington, D.C.), plans C&R 31–4–45 and C&R 40–15–6H.

[9] Transcript of original offsets, The Josiah Fox Papers (Peabody Marine Museum, Salem, Massachusetts), no. 36: Wesson's Calendar. ERNEST J. WESSON, *A Calendar of the Papers of Josiah Fox* (Mansfield, Ohio: Privately published, 1933) is used for an index.

[10] *American State Papers,* vol. 1.

[11] FRANK M. BENNETT, *The Steam Navy of the United States* (Pittsburgh: Warren & Co., Publishers, 1896), p. 141.

[12] CHARLES OSCAR PAULLIN, *Paullin's History of Naval Administration 1775–1911* (Annapolis, Maryland: U.S. Naval Institute, 1968), pp. 343–345.

[13] Plans of *Peacock, Erie, Macedonian,* and *Congress,* before and after rebuilding, will be found in HOWARD I. CHAPELLE, op. cit. (footnote 4).

[14] *Transactions of the Society of Naval Architects and Marine Engineers* (1914) vol. 22, pp. 139–155.

[15] Transcription of "Dimensions of Frigates Congress and Constellation of each, 36 Guns taken off the Mould loft floor by Josiah Fox—1794 by which those ships were Constructed," The Josiah Fox Papers (Peabody Marine Museum, Salem, Massachusetts), no. 36, pp. 1–27. There is much of the Fox-Truxtun correspondence in this collection dealing with the *Constellation.*

[16] *American State Papers,* vol. 1 (footnote 2), pp. 13–17.

[17] *Newport Navalog* (U.S. Naval Station, Newport, R.I.), Friday 26 January 1946.

[18] The card index in the plan files of the U.S. Navy Records on Construction and Repair (National Archives, Washington, D.C.) show the original plan collection.

[19] THEODORE ROOSEVELT, *Naval War of 1812,* 3rd ed. (New York: 1883).

[20] Incidentally, the word "design," applied to the drawing or the modeling of a ship, was not used in 18th-century books on naval architecture and shipbuilding in the English language.

[21] *The Pennsylvania Magazine of History and Biography* (July 1964), vol. LXXXVIII, no. 3, pp. 316–327.

[22] *The Journal of American History* (1st quarter, 1908), vol. II, no. 1, pp. 102–112.

[23] Record Group 19: Records of the Bureau of Ships (National Archives, Washington, D.C.), C&R 107–13–4B.

[24] Longitudinal timbers in a wooden hull are "scarphed," not "spliced"; the only plank "scarphed" in the wale strakes and the celing stringers.

[25] *Transactions of the Society of Naval Architects and Marine Engineers* (1914), vol. 22, pp. 139–155.

[26] Polland, op. cit. (footnote 2).

[27] EUGENE S. FERGUSON, *Truxtun of the Constellation, The Life of Commodore Thomas Truxtun, U.S. Navy 1755–1822* (Baltimore, Maryland: Johns Hopkins Press 1956), p. 126.

[28] A marine railway was built at Washington Navy Yard about 1818, but this appears to have been too small to haul a large frigate.

PART 2

Comments on
"The Story of the *Constellation*"

Introduction

O N 15 NOVEMBER 1968 the *Constellation* Restoration Committee of Baltimore received from the Director of the Smithsonian Institution Press a 64-page document over the name of Howard I. Chapelle. The delivery of that document was the result of a proposal requiring that this writer review the manuscript and prepare a rebuttal stating the views of the *Constellation* Committee concerning the background of the Frigate *Constellation*.

Over the past ten years, Mr. Chapelle has questioned the authenticity of the Frigate *Constellation* now in Baltimore Harbor as well as the integrity of those most intimately connected with the restoration.

If the reader's hopes include a similar barrage of undignified language in rebuttal to Mr. Chapelle, the following pages will contain many disappointments. When the reader finally closes the cover here, it is this writer's hope that he will have also observed some of the gentlemanly rules of conduct for it is only necessary to present the facts and to prove the point, and this we will proceed to do.

Before proceeding to the evaluation of Mr. Chapelle's manuscript and a formal presentation of our views, the reader should be acquainted with certain facts for we must be ever vigilant to guard against the semantics so often employed to twist those facts.

In March 1961, the *Constellation* Committee published an article in the Maryland Historical Magazine presenting its views for the first time on this subject.[1] Several conclusions therein leaned heavily upon documents which were transcribed from the originals that were purportedly lost or destroyed. Several typewritten copies have since been found to be of a questionable nature and have been discarded. This writer was one of the contributors to that article which, considering the restrictions of space in a magazine, is a rather thorough research outline on the subject of the *Constellation* frigate. Speaking for the Committee, the information contained therein was set down in every instance in good faith. I cannot state that I was in agreement with each conclusion, for I was not. Recognizing the weaknesses of that article, I began work on a

---

Leon D. Polland is Chief of Construction and Repair of the Frigate Constellation, Constellation *Restoration Committee of Baltimore, and Naval Architect, Division of Engineering, Office of Ship Construction, Maritime Administration, United States Department of Commerce.*

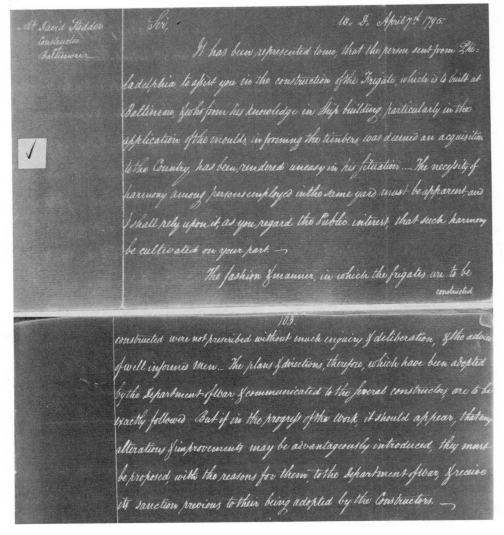

FIGURE 1.—Letter from the War Office to David Stodder, 7 April 1796 (National Archives, Washington, D.C., Record Group 45, Entry 374, Letters sent concerning Naval matters, October 1790–June 1798).

more comprehensive vehicle of my own, embodying our archeological findings as well as the documentary research in various repositories.

On 7 May 1966 this writer was granted the privilege of presenting his 131-page paper before the Chesapeake and Hampton Roads Section of the Society of Naval Architects and Marine Engineers (S.N.A.M.E.). Since that date, every report and comment on that paper brought to the attention of this office has been of approval. The second edition has been equally well received.[2]

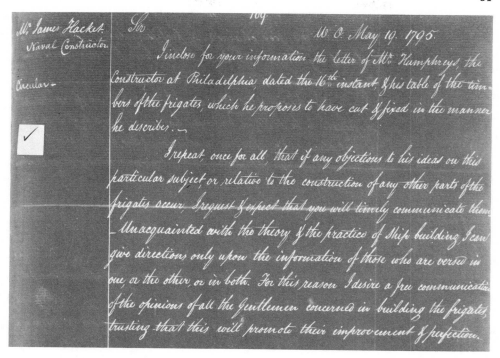

FIGURE 2.—Letter from the Secretary of the Navy to James Hacket, 19 May 1795 (National Archives, Washington, D.C., Record Group 45, Entry 374, Letters sent concerning Naval matters, October 1790–June 1798).

It was not until 1968 that Mr. Chapelle prepared a response to our 1961 article, questioning the documentation which had been accepted to begin with in good faith on the part of this committee. This writer long ago has said such documents were presented solely on the basis of their existence.

Referring to my paper of 7 May 1966 Mr. Chapelle says "The result is much repetition of the Maryland Historical Magazine article claims. . . ." Mr. Chapelle continues to say that the paper presents this writer's own design for the conversion of a sloop-of-war to a frigate.

The chief criticism is directed at several documents which appear to be typewritten transcriptions of original papers. These are the papers which this committee has reviewed and subsequently discarded since their publication by the Maryland Historical Society Magazine eight years ago.

There are, of course, other such documents which this author feels cannot be cast out.[3] The information contained in such papers is sometimes repeated in other documents located hundreds of miles distant which often infers a basis or at least a connection for the transcription. We cannot arbitrarily discount letters, sketches, and plans when they do not entirely reflect professional language or for that matter necessarily agree with our views. Neither can we believe that papers found in various and wide-

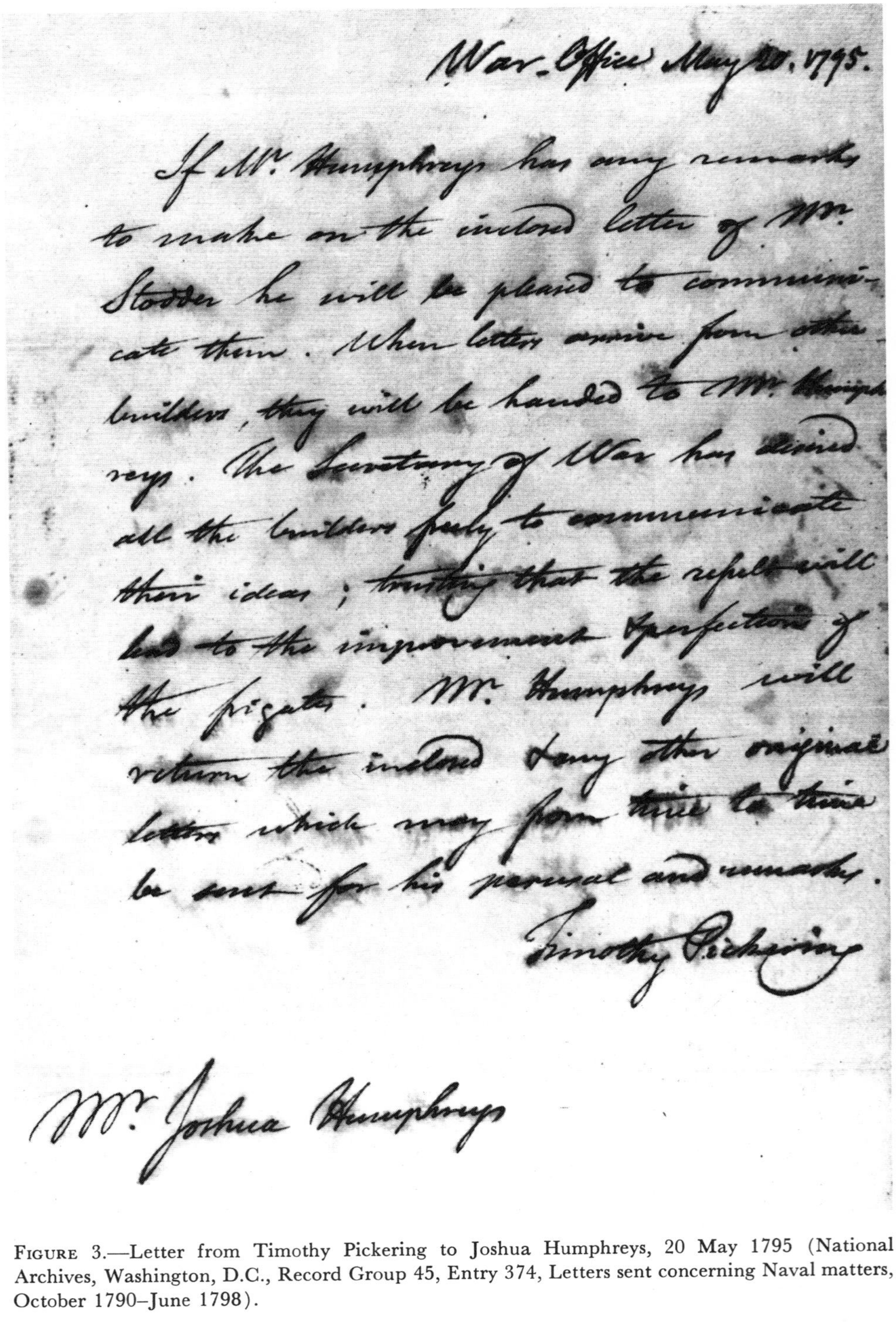

War-Office May 20. 1795.

If Mr. Humphreys has any remarks to make on the inclosed letter of Mr. Stodder he will be pleased to communicate them. When letters arrive from other builders, they will be handed to Mr. Humphreys. The Secretary of War has desired all the builders freely to communicate their ideas; trusting that the result will lead to the improvement & perfection of the frigates. Mr. Humphreys will return the inclosed & any other original letters which may from time to time be sent for his perusal and remarks.

Timothy Pickering

Mr. Joshua Humphreys

FIGURE 3.—Letter from Timothy Pickering to Joshua Humphreys, 20 May 1795 (National Archives, Washington, D.C., Record Group 45, Entry 374, Letters sent concerning Naval matters, October 1790–June 1798).

spread repositories can have been (except in isolated cases) placed in those files for any but the most valid of reasons; and we are speaking now of, in addition to the Newport Naval Training Station in Rhode Island, such institutions as the Library of Congress, the National Archives, the Franklin D. Roosevelt Library, the Department of Naval History, and various historical societies.

In any event, the few transcribed papers presented here as evidence (even though that evidence be secondary) are submitted on the basis of their very existence.[4] As sometimes happens, this may be as close to the truth as we can get. Fortunately, such is not the case, since enough valid evidence exists in the remaining original documents as well as in the physical structure of the ship to indicate this *Constellation* as having been reconstructed from Truxtun's own ship. She has never lost her identity.

As is often the case in a work of this nature, it is not possible to gather all the material here without the help of able and dedicated assistance. In this effort, the author called upon Mr. Michael Morgan, historian of the Construction and Repair Committee for the early records of United States ships. His enthusiastic response resulted in the following narration regarding the construction of the *Chesapeake* in Norfolk, as well as many of our observations on the character of Thomas Truxtun.

In the following pages, we shall present the case for the historical and structural integrity of the *Constellation* frigate of Baltimore. This committee was limited to less than three months in which to present that case. This writer, of course, would have preferred an additional three months which could have been profitably used. He is, however, grateful to the Smithsonian Institution for the opportunity to put together the following notes on behalf of the *Constellation*.

It is, of course, necessary to "define the problem" in order that the reader may draw his conclusions based upon the material presented. The reader may note at least three hypotheses by Mr. Chapelle and by this writer. He may conclude that the subject of this work, the Frigate *Constellation* was (1) broken up completely and destroyed in 1853–55 and the present ship is the result of a completely new construction; (2) hauled up and lengthened by twelve feet just forward of the midbody; (3) lengthened as above but completely torn down in the process, retaining only the keel.

It is apparent that the two latter conclusions would infer the continuous existence of the Frigate, differing only in degree of change. We are aware, too, that even the *Constitution* now carries but a portion of her original keel, although she has not lost her original lines.

Mr. Chapelle does not accept as valid evidence the employment of transcribed documents which indicate some disagreement in design between David Stodder, the Baltimore builder, and Joshua Humphreys, who submitted the preliminary draught drawn by William Doughty. Further, basic departures from the original draught are indicated in the hull structure of the ship.

Difficulties at Baltimore, as well as elsewhere (Figures 1–3) were not exceptional and could lead to modifications of original ideas.

Comments

Page 4

Mr. Chapelle states that this committee presents its 1961 claims [5] based chiefly on a brief prepared by Franklin Delano Roosevelt and "Another presentation was made in a paper read before a meeting of an American professional society's sections in 1966, supplementing the 1961 publication." This may be somewhat misleading to the reader, as the 1961 publication, based on Franklin Delano Roosevelt's memorandum was presented as a magazine article in the available space of *16* pages. In 1966, the presentation to the Society of Naval Architects and Marine Engineers contained *131* pages, only a small part of which traces its origin to Roosevelt's writings. The second edition of that paper, is now 188 pages in book form. Quite a "supplement" to a magazine article!

Page 7

Mr. Chapelle states that on 27 March 1794 Congress authorized the construction of six frigates, three of 44 guns and three of 36 guns. A simple reading of the authorization act reveals that Congress authorized *four* 44s and *two* 36s.[6] This may seem to be a minor error, but Mr. Chapelle builds upon it to create an argument for his position that the *Constellation* was built according to the official plans. This contention is summarized on page 31 of Mr. Chapelle's paper. While discussing the Fox statement of 27 November 1826 Mr. Chapelle, commenting on Fox's claim that timber prepared for the Norfolk frigate had been used to finish the *Constellation* says, "Since the Norfolk ship was one of the three 36s on the official draught it is obvious that the official design was used for the Baltimore frigate since the timbers on official design moulds could be used." This might be a strong argument, except for the fact that the Norfolk ship was a 44 and not a 36.[7] The history of the frigate built at Norfolk is rather muddled and calls for a detailed examination.

The distribution of the six frigates is clearly stated in a letter from the Secretary of War to the House of Representatives on 29 December 1794. In this letter, the Secretary reports on the progress of the six ships and he states that the 44s were to be built at Philadelphia, New York, Boston, and Norfolk. The 36s were to be built at Baltimore and Portsmouth, New Hampshire.[8] A year later another progress report was made, from which the following is the report on the Norfolk ship:

64

Statement of the progress made in building a frigate, to carry forty-four guns, at Norfolk, under the direction of Mr. Josiah Fox, Naval Constructor, and Captain Richard Dale, Superintendent.

The keel is completed and laid on the blocks; the pieces are scarfed and bolted to each other in the best manner. The stern frame is complete and ready for raising. More than two-thirds of the live oak for the frame is arrived, which is worked to the various moulds; great part of the timbers are bolted together in frames, and are ready for raising. The gun deck and the lower deck are all finished, and are ready to put into the ship. The plank for the decks is not yet arrived. The outside plank, as likewise the ceiling, are preparing, and some part have been delivered. All the copper necessary for securing the various parts of the ship together, and for the sheathing the bottom, is in the public stores. The keelson and midship dead woods are complete. The masts, bowsprit, yards and all the other spars, are cut, and several of them are received at the yard. The carlings, ledges, coamings for the hatchways, and the partners for the mast, are now in hand. The iron work for the hull and materials are getting ready. The caboose, with a hearth, forge armorer's tools, spare coppers, boilers, &c. are complete. All the necessary contracts are entered into by the agent, and the articles contracted for are daily arriving.[9]

From this report, it can be seen that quite a bit of work was done on the Norfolk ship before peace was made with Algiers. According to the terms of the original authorization act, work was to cease on the frigates if peace was made with Algiers. On 20 April 1796, however, Congress approved the completion of three of the frigates (*Constitution, United States, Constellation*) and the President was authorized to sell those perishable materials that were not needed to complete the remaining three ships. The other materials were to be stored until they were needed.[10]

It is at this point that Fox maintains that the material from the discontinued ship at Norfolk was sent to Baltimore to complete the *Constellation*. This could be true, but if it is, then the timber had to be reworked since the Norfolk ship was a 44 and the Baltimore ship a 36.

On 16 July 1798 Congress authorized the building of the other three frigates (*Chesapeake, Congress,* and *President*) and authorized the President to use any materials on hand for these ships.[11] It appears that the original work that had been started on the Norfolk ship had been dismantled and the construction was resumed in 1798. This second vessel laid down at Norfolk was nominally a 44 but she was built to a different design from the other 44s. In his *History of the American Sailing Navy,* page 135, Mr. Chapelle has the following to say about her:

When work stopped on the frigates she was so little advanced that the order in effect canceled her construction. Fox had joined with Truxtun and others in objecting to the size of the 44-gun frigates, and their arguments had much effect on the authorities. As a result Fox was permitted to prepare a new design for a 44, of reduced size, that would have the approval of Truxtun and other objectors. The authorization for the revised design does not exist (at least it has not been found), but the correspondence shows that the Secretary of the Navy was aware that the new ship was smaller than the previous 44s for he inquired as to her dimensions and tonnage when she was under construction. Among the Fox Papers there is a drawing, entitled *Congress,* which may be her building plan. The new ship was launched, under the name *Chesapeake* on June 20, 1799.

There are several points to be made about this passage. The frigate *Chesapeake* was launched on 2 December 1799 not 20 June 1799.[12] Mr. Chapelle has confused the frigate with a sloop built under the name *Chesapeake* but this name was changed to *Patapsco*.[13] The most interesting part of this passage from Mr. Chapelle's book is the statement that the *Chesapeake* was built to a new design and the authorization for that new design has not been located. Two letters shed additional light on this subject.

The first is from Abashai Thomas for the Secretary of the Navy to Josiah Fox and states as follows:

> Sir Since I have been in the Navy Office I have always considered the Chesapeake as calculated to carry 30–18 pounders & 14 Twelves. Today it has been discovered that she was originally intended to carry 28–18 pounders and 16 nines—I cannot find that any orders have been given to alter her from the first design, & yet the letter covering directions to you to have the Carriages made designates 12 pounders—As the Guns are now preparing & will soon be ready to send off—I am directed by the Secretary to request that you will be pleased as soon as may be to forward to this Office correct information on the subject. . . .
>
> P.S. On Shewing this letter to Mr. Stoddert, he observed that he had determined the Quarter Deck Guns should be 9 pounders—therefore it is only the numbers we want—Dimensions for making the Carriages are inclosed this day to Mr. Pennock. . . .[14]

The above letter is dated 26 October 1799 as is the following letter from the Secretary of the Navy to William Pennock:

> Sir A Mistake has been made in giving directions for making the Carriages for the Guns of the Chesapeake—She is to mount Eighteen pounders & nine pounders—You will please to have the Carriages made accordingly. . . .
>
> PS—Be pleased to inform me as early as may be whether the Frigate is pierced for 30 or 28 Guns on the Gun Deck, and what number on the Quarter Deck &c. The dimensions of the Nine Pounders are enclosed. . . .[15]

These letters indicate that not only were changes made in the design of the Chesapeake but also that authorization for such changes could not be found in 1799. Notice the confusion that existed in the Secretary of the Navy's office as to the number of guns *Chesapeake* carried on her gun deck, where a change in the number of gunports was a major change in the ship. Mr. Chapelle accepts these changes in the *Chesapeake* even though no authorization for them exists. He does not, however, accept changes in the design of the *Constellation* (changes that caused less confusion than those made on the *Chesapeake*) on the grounds that no record of the authorization for such changes can be found.

Page 11

The construction of ships' draughts are irrelevant to the discussion at hand.

Page 12

Mr. Chapelle's comment concerning the original offsets of this ship, "now represented in the Fox papers at Salem, Massachusetts, by a museum transcript, the original having been extracted unlawfully by a recent visitor" does not go unnoticed. The intent and meaning is clear enough and we hope that he will soon have the opportunity to elaborate upon this interesting statement.

Page 13

Once again, it is not quite understood how a description of diagonal planking and dagger knees, etc., bears upon the question at hand: the authentic nature of the *Constellation* frigate of Baltimore.

Page 14

We note Mr. Chapelle's statement that *"rebuilding* began by hauling the ship ashore" (italics mine). At least there is agreement on that point; however, rebuilding does not imply the *breaking up* of a ship: [16]

Something didn't sound right! Hauled up? Was a ship 'hauled clear' of the water for dismantling? Certainly not. It has always been the practice to disassemble the top hamper and upper works with the ship afloat. As weight is removed from the topsides, the hulk rises in the water allowing dismantling to the floor timbers whereupon the remaining keel assembly is easily hauled and torn apart for salvage. This is the procedure to this very day.

This writer, within recent years had an opportunity to take part in dismantling the last United States Battleship, *Kentucky,* and the above procedure was followed just as it was a century before. At this point, let us at least establish that the ship was, indeed, hauled up,[17] and let us fix the date (see Figure 4).

In attempting to build a case for the construction of new ships to replace original vessels through the Navy's "manipulation" of funds, Mr. Chapelle reaches back to the case of the *John Adams,* the *Macedonian,* and the *Congress.* We can find no record of the Navy *denying* the facts that the original ships were broken up and new ships built.

It may be appropriate here to voice the sentiments of this writer on the wisdom of employing records of ships other than the *Constellation* to prove a point.

From page 93 in the Summary of this writer's paper of 7 May 1966:

As befits a work of this nature, the following summary is appended. Data contributing certain and direct validity is listed here. Transcriptions will not be considered *nor will evidence be presented pertaining to any but this ship* [italic added]. It follows that typewritten unsigned documents may be presented as secondary evidence only when supported by a primary source.

Again it will not be considered valid to state that the files of another ship, or other ships, indicate structural histories which have not been found to follow here. The question has been, "What happened to *this* ship?"

In the face of the foregoing, what happened to the *Peacock,* the *Adams,* the *Macedonian,* the *Congress,* the *Cyane,* etc., is of passing moment. It follows that this writer will not consider valid here, evidence pertaining to ships other than the *Constellation.* That being the case, we must discount several large segments of extraneous matter from Mr. Chapelle's manuscript.

It may be well to say also that it is universally agreed that the ship, from her launching until the day she entered Gosport the North Slip over half a century later, was the original *Constellation.* If this is so, interpretation of the documents involved is irrelevant.

Page 16

Here Mr. Chapelle states that the 74-gun *Franklin* scheduled to be razeed was instead "rebuilt" (Mr. Chapelle's quotes) meaning, of course, that she was surreptitiously built entirely as a new ship. Again, we can find no evidence that the Navy denies the fact that this was a new ship and as Mr. Chapelle states, "Bennet says she was built entirely with maintenance funds."

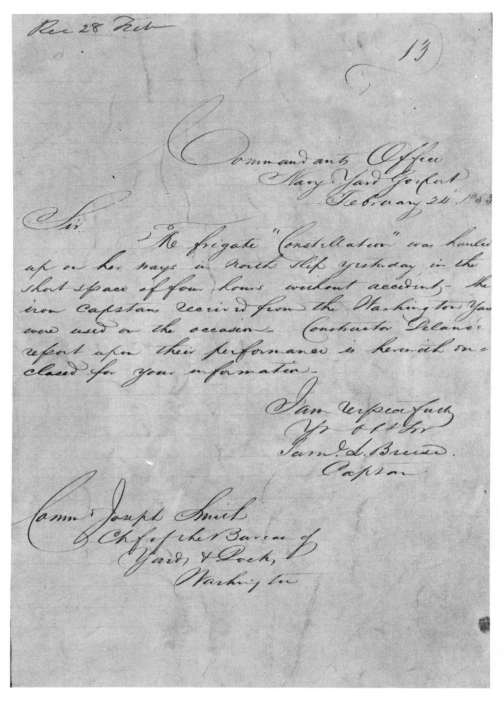

FIGURE 4.—Letter from Samuel S. Breese to Joseph Smith, 24 February 1853
(National Archives, Washington, D.C., Record Group 19).

Page 18

Among other misleading statements by Mr. Chapelle, we find that Roosevelt has incorrectly determined that Stodder "let it be known that he disagreed with the official design, did not respect Humphreys as a designer and would accept no orders from Truxtun." The probable source is given in the Fox Papers, Fox to Truxtun 2 April 1795 and ". . . this is too late a date for any substitution in design, for the timber required in the official design had begun to arrive in the yard. Although the above Fox letter is dated 2 April 1795, we have no indication that Stodder made his statement *on that date; only that Fox signed his own letter on that date.* Stodder may or may not have, made his statement long before and we should remember, too, that this was secondhand information. It should be especially noted that one of the major considerations of Mr. Chapelle's discussion is that of the frame spacing. This will be discussed at greater length in the following pages. For the moment, this writer will observe that the timber and room turned out to be something other than one would expect if we are to believe that the Humphreys' draught (really the Doughty draught) of 1794 was followed by the builder. Further, it should be emphasized that the existence of a drawing does not indicate the existence of a structure. This, too, will be discussed at length as our discussion develops.

The change in frame spacing and structure described by Franklin Delano Roosevelt actually did take place as we shall attempt to prove, although he left little for us to find in the way of his own source material. We do not know from where his information was derived but we do have the ship in Baltimore Harbor and as Mr. Roosevelt said, she "was the work of one David Stodder. . . ." Mr. Chapelle takes the liberty of stating that *"it appears* that Stodder could have had no time for the . . . substitution of design . . . had the situation described by Roosevelt actually existed" (italics mine). In the experience of this writer in serious research, it just "appears" that the use of that word should be stressed as suggestive of a fact, since it "appears" that the truth is not really known. The fact is it "appears' that changes *were* made in the structure although records no longer exist, unless we choose to investigate the one greatest, most revealing record of all—the ship now in Baltimore Harbor. It is sad to relate that Mr. Chapelle, to our knowledge, in more than 20 years has not taken the time to visit the *Constellation.* To elaborate for a moment on the above observation, a "visit" to the ship is a rather mild term. Nothing short of a full fledged survey would reveal anything close to the many answers that this hull might contain within her planks.

This writer has participated in several dozen ship surveys which, by the way, entail dirty coveralls, much sweat and grime, freezing weather and Hades hot summers, in the bowels of the vessel—and all the while making notes and sketches which he will later transcribe to permanent records. A far cry from one depending upon his books for all the answers. It must be quite obvious that only a combination of the two can provide the reader with the answers he seeks, and this combination has long since become a way of life for the *Constellation* Construction and Repair Committee.

Mr. Chapelle tells us "It is evident that Roosevelt was unacquainted with the temperment of Truxtun, who was a very proud man, with a keen sense of duty, and who was also meticulous in demanding recognition of his authority. To suggest that this man would stand aside, supinely, in any situation as has been described, is ludicrous."

This is a rather heavy handed reading of Truxtun's character. It is true that Truxtun was often dogmatic in his dealings with others, but it is a restricted view of Truxtun's character. In reality, he was a complex man.

During *Constellation's* initial cruise, Truxtun discovered that his second lieutenant, William Cowper, was inattentive to duty, allowing the sails to go untrimmed, the rigging to go slack and lines to be dragged in the water. On several occasions Truxtun brought these matters to Cowper's attention, but the lieutenant failed to correct them in the course of events. Truxtun wrote Cowper a note telling him in no uncertain terms that these matters must be corrected. This letter included the following passage:

> I have been told, that you say it would take an Attorney, to learn, and retain the Instructions in Print, I have only to observe, that when a School Boy at a Vacation, I have had three Times as much assigned me as a Task, and did not think it difficult.
>
> It is unnecessary for me at present to add, I therefore shall expect in the future the Orders of the Ship more attended to, and a Consistency more in Character observed.[18]

Cowper replied to Truxtun's note with a letter of his own, which is now lost. Truxtun, however, again replied to Cowper's note and this second letter of Truxtun's appears in the Naval records.[19] At this point, Mr. Chapelle's interpretation of Truxtun's character should be considered and its validity tested in the light of the Captain's reply. According to Mr. Chapelle, we would expect a similar letter to the one quoted above; a letter in which Truxtun would demand "meticulous recognition of his authority." The reverse is true. In Truxtun's second letter, he notes the inexperience of the officers and he accepts Cowper's promises, which apparently were made in the lost letter.

Truxtun ends with the following paragraph:

> Good Subordination must always be strictly kept up, among a Number of Men, but in being strict in Discipline, Justness must not be forgotten, or the Savage Character had Recourse to. Ordering of Punishment is to a Man possessing the Principles of a Gentlemen, always painful, and however irritable he may become from vexatious Circumstances, frequently occurring; the more he reflects, and the less frequent his Punishments are, the better; In fact they should only happen, when indispensably necessary, and their Effect will be the greater.[20]

This certainly is not the writing of a man with an excessively proud nature that Mr. Chapelle suggests. Truxtun was not that simple a man. This, on the other hand, is not to suggest that Truxtun would have allowed Stodder to make any changes in the plans without question. Truxtun would have questioned these changes, but in an orderly manner. An examination of an incident that occurred in 1800 will demonstrate how Truxtun might have handled Stodder in 1795.

As Mr. Chapelle states, Truxtun had a meticulous sense of duty which he applied not only to others but to himself as well. In 1800, the frigate *Congress* was dismasted during a storm and Truxtun was appointed president of a court of inquiry to investigate the circumstances. While the court of inquiry was being arranged, several members of the crew of the *Congress* attempted to incite their shipmates to mutiny. Truxtun apparently asked for authority to order a court martial for these men, as can be seen from the following letter from the Secretary of the Navy Stoddart to Truxtun, dated 15 April 1800:

Captain Sever had reported to me, the mutinous conduct of some of the Crew of the Frigate *Congress*—As Commander of the Squadron, you might have ordered a Court Martial at once, without appealing, to me, & I am sorry you did not do it. I do not like this method of appealing to the head of the Department, by officers, who are themselves competent to the object of appeal—I have now directed Captain Sever to apply to you for a Court Martial, which be please to order.[21]

It is evident that Truxtun had been unsure of his authority and had asked Stoddart for a clarification. In 1795 a similar situation existed and Truxtun reacted similarly as an examination of the following exchange of letters shows.

On 2 April 1795 Josiah Fox wrote the following letter to Truxtun:

. . . a few weeks ago I happened to meet with a Builder who resides at Kensington (and who I apprehend a person of Character & Reputation) the Subject of our Discourse turning on the Frigates, which are now building in the United States the person informed me he had been in company with Builder Stodder of Baltimore a few days before (I believe at Kensington) who told him he had seen the Draught of the Frigates which he appeared to dispise [sic] and told the said person he knew how to Draught & Model the Frigates much better than the persons who were employed by the Secretary of War for that purpose & that he would not build the Frigate at Baltimore agreeable to the Draught nor War Office directions—but would do just as he pleased, saying he could build a Ship better than any other person or an expression somewhat similar, therefore should not pay any attention to the Moulds or Bevellings sent him for the purpose of Building the said Frigate, neither would he act in Conformity to Directions from any persons appointed to Superintend the aforesaid Frigate—there were many other expressions which has escaped my memory—as it appeared to give the aforesaid person some reasonable Grounds for Supposing the Constructor of the Navy of the U.S. & Capt who is appointed to superintend the Building were deficient in abilites [sic] to conduct the Business and tending also to convey prejudices against the Office of the executive department of Government, I think it my duty to acquaint you of those circumstances in order to prevent any bad consequences that might result from such proceedings and likewise to let you Know that if any alterations should be made in the Said Frigate (not by express order of the Department of War) that it was premeditated by Builder Stodder previous to Building the Said Frigate—I think Samuel Owner [Bower?] was present at the time this Conversation passed [22]

Truxtun's response to this letter is similar to his reaction during the situation aboard the *Congress* in 1800. In both cases, he seemed to be unsure of his authority and he wrote to his superiors for clarification. Although Truxtun's letter is apparently lost, its content can be inferred by the reply from the War Department. This letter to Truxtun was written on 7 April 1795. It acknowledges Truxton's letter of the previous day and states that the instructions of the Secretary of War to the constructors have been examined and these instructions give the authority to the superintendent, confining a constructor to the plans. If a deviation from the plans was made, the superintendent should file a report to the Secretary of War, who would compel conformity or discharge the constructor.[23]

With the authority to deal with any deviation in the plans clarified, Truxtun set out to deal with Stodder. Again, unfortunately, Truxtun's letter is lost but Stodder's reply of 14 April 1795 (see p. 75) makes it clear that Truxtun had questioned some of the changes. Our comments will follow in proper sequence.

Page 19

This writer must again take exception to Mr. Chapelle's use of the statement that "Aside from the effects of her two battles with French frigates there is no official record *yet found* of any serious damage from gunfire" (italics mine). This does not indicate that there was no damage; only that no records have yet been found. Although the above example is one of minor significance, Mr. Chapelle often uses this phraseology as a valid statement of fact.

Mr. Chapelle's criticism of Mr. Roosevelt's "curiously nonprofessional language" is, in most instances, unfair and often attempts to show himself in a contrasting light of the cold efficient professional. The reader should not be deceived by these tactics which seek to place the chosen target in a defensive attitude. The psychological reaction of the reader or the observer is "supposed" to be one which will look to the obvious professional for the true facts and who is obviously the professional, the expert in each case? Mr. Chapelle, of course, who is now free to pass judgment.

Mr. Chapelle emphasizes the nomenclature used by Mr. Roosevelt and almost everyone else who takes a view opposite to his own. Here we note that Roosevelt's "old line and wound works" does not appear in the nautical dictionaries, indicating, of course, that the late President was an unprofessional (and unwelcome) intruder. Throughout Mr. Chapelle's manuscript, he pounds away at the unprofessional language employed by transcribers when the truth is that, in many cases, they could not decipher the old English handwriting in the original documents. This is especially true in cases where technical terms are employed. To illustrate this point, the reader has only to glance at the papers reproduced within these pages.

There have been typewritten sheets submitted here as "true transcribed copies" and indeed we accepted some in good faith—in 1961, but they have since been discarded by us as invalid. If, however, there is a chance that they may be traced to a valid source, then we have no choice but to accept them for *what they are* on the very basis of their existence.[24] It will be shown, however, that this case does not rest upon such evidence.

Now let us analyze Roosevelt's "old line and wound works," which appears to have a somewhat explosive effect upon Mr. Chapelle. As he so correctly points out after a thorough perusal of his dictionaries, "bands of hemp rope around built-up masts and spars were called 'wooldings', . . ." Although this writer has the same nautical dictionaries close at hand, I immediately understood Mr. Roosevelt's meaning of ". . . line and wound works" without retreating to my library. As is so often the case in the treatment of naval nomenclature, the old terms often do not sufficiently describe the item or detail, in which case, it is sometimes prudent to provide a more descriptive terminology when addressing an audience.

While Mr. Roosevelt may, or may not, have been familiar with "wooldings" and unfortunately, of course, he is not around to defend himself, he did find a near perfect description—and in only four words!

This writer must go on record here as often being guilty of the same "crime"— and I might add that I am still actively engaged in the art of shipbuilding and closely connected with several modern shipyards. It is by no means unnatural to revert to "descriptive nomenclature" when addressing laymen or even people within the same organization but with varying professions and trades—and nomenclature of their own.

Mr. Chapelle expends much time and paper berating Mr. Roosevelt and the transcribers for their ignorance. Actually, in most cases, the transcribers did the best they could and we are thankful that they at least preserved the gist of the message.

Page 20

Mr. Roosevelt, in describing the condition of *Constellation* before the 1853–55 repair, tells us that "Her keel was warped, high in the center and low on the ends," meaning, of course, that the ship was hogged, and continues ". . . a shoe . . . was made . . . to straighten it." From this, Mr. Chapelle gathers that "Roosevelt imagined the hog in the keel . . . would be *built into the new vessel*" (italics mine)!

Page 21

Regarding a visual inspection of *Constellation*'s timbers, we are told by Mr. Chapelle that in the 113 years of her "existence," from 1855 to the present time, "the appearance of her timbers could readily give the impression of great age." How right he is! It is certainly unfortunate that he has never been aboard during the fifteen years that this committee has held custody of the ship. We may have had the opportunity to point out to him many good examples of the 113 year old timbers on the gun decks as well as on the berth deck. As a matter of fact, a careful comparison of coloring and texture in the hatch coamings on those decks, as well as the breast hooks, with their counterparts below on the orlop level and in the hold indicate a substantial difference in age. The oak timber below is easily identified by its darker color, as much *older* in the ship.

Mr. Chapelle tells us (p. 21) that "it is naive to accept these [dated timbers and metal fastenings] as evidence. . . ." and that these are the "byproducts of numerous repairs and overenthusiasm on the part of workmen."

In the condensation of my 1966 paper which forms the second section of this effort, we have taken the opportunity to insert several additional comments. We shall present a professional analysis of the copper hull fastening bolts (p. 141) withdrawn from the *Constellation*.

Mr. Chapelle contends that it could not have required "hundreds of men" to help haul up *Constellation* at Gosport as Mr. Roosevelt claimed because the Navy Yard had geared capstans and other mechanical aids. Mr. Chapelle notes also that "the ship would actually have . . . ballast removed" before hauling. So again, we are reminded that Mr. Roosevelt imagined the entire operation. Attention is called to the two entries from the Gosport Log, dated 23 February 1853 and 24 February 1853.[26] The first entry includes *"8 overseers & 153 white laborers* with all the mechanics . . . hauling up Frigate *Constellation*" (italics mine). The second entry the next day includes the notation "landing ballast from *Constellation*" (Figure 5).

Page 22

Mr. Chapelle states that, "It is not true, of course, that either the frigate or the existing corvette was very sharp in the entrance; neither supports any claim of 'futuristic thinking'. . . ." To counter this unsupported statement, we must offer the letter of Truxtun to Livingston, 22 May 1798: ". . . his new ideas in the *form of the bow* will most likely increase the speed through the water of the hull. . . ."[25] (italics mine). On page 30, Mr. Chapelle introduces another letter from Truxtun's correspondence relating to sharpness in her *bottom* after which he concludes that "this *seems* to mean . . . *deadrise*" (italics mine)!

Mr. Chapelle contends that "the decision was made to restore the *Constitution* (instead of the *Constellation*)" after an evaluation of Mr. Roosevelt's papers written in 1914 and 1918. Mr. Chapelle further presents Secretary Daniels memorandum to Mr. Roosevelt dated 18 December 1918. It may be well to note that *Constitution* was not restored until many years later (1929–1930). Actually, when the moment arrived to make the choice between the two ships, the Navy made note of the fact that *Constitution,* although many times rebuilt, still retained her square stern and original length. Further, *Constitution,* originally built at Boston was to be displayed there as a memorial to the Navy and as a reminder to all of the proud shipbuilding heritage of the people of that city. On the other hand, *Constellation,* although in much

FIGURE 5.—Entries from Gosport Log, signed by A. T. Young and dated 23 and 24 February 1853, respectively (National Archives, Washington, D.C., Record Group 71).

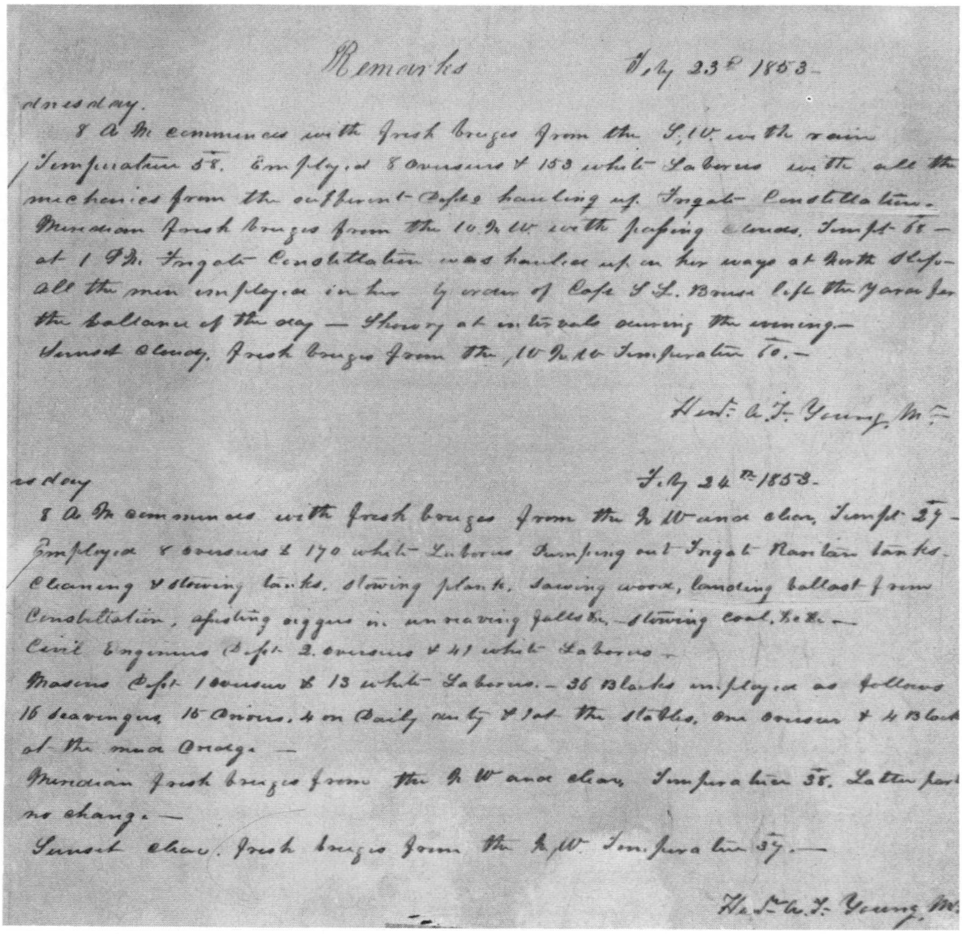
Remarks Feby 23d 1853-
dnesday.
8 A M commences with fresh breezes from the S.W. with rain
Temperature 58. Employed 8 Overseers & 153 white Laborers with all the
mechanics from the different Depts hauling up Frigate Constellation.
Meridian fresh breezes from the N.W. with passing clouds. Tempt 58 –
at 1 P.M. Frigate Constellation was hauled up on her ways at North Slip–
All the men employed in her by order of Capt S. L. Breese left the Yard for
the ballance of the day – Showery at intervals during the evening.–
Sunset cloudy. fresh breezes from the N.W. Temperature 60.–
Hent: A. T. Young, M.

esday Feby 24th 1853-
8 A M commences with fresh breezes from the N W and clear. Tempt 27 –
Employed 8 overseers & 170 white Laborers Pumping out Frigate Raritan tanks.
Cleaning & stowing tanks, stowing plank, sawing wood, landing ballast from
Constellation, assisting riggers in unreaving falls &c.– stowing coal, &c &c –
Civil Engineers Dept 2 overseers & 41 white Laborers –
Masons Dept 1 overseer & 13 white Laborers.– 36 Blacks employed as follows
16 scavengers 15 Drivers. 4 on Daily duty & 1 at the stables, one overseer & 4 Black
at the mud Dredge. –
Meridian fresh breezes from the N W and clear. Temperature 38. Latter part
no change. –
Sunset clear. fresh breezes from the N.W. Temperature 37.–
Hent. A. T. Young, M.

better physical condition, had been modernized with 12 feet added to her length, and her stern, long ago rounded to an elliptical curve; and there is more to this rounded stern than may meet the eye, as we shall soon see.

Page 23

Mr. Chapelle discusses the "Documentation of the Roosevelt Brief." As we have already pointed out, the reader should be fully aware that the article in question was published in *March of 1961*. Subsequent recognition of several deficiencies in that article led to the presentation of a paper before the Society of Naval Architects and Marine Engineers (S.N.A.M.E.) in 1966. Controversy over a magazine article, now generally unavailable and superseded by a much more comprehensive work, would not further the aims of this discussion. As this report develops, we shall include a condensation of the paper of 7 May 1966, which we believe will provide enough additional information to inform the reader of the overall situation.

Page 25

Mr. Chapelle invites our attention to the "time factor"; "timber for the authorized design was coming into the yard. So it was far too late for any change in hull design." He further contends that it was impractical to alter the "official" moulds and bevels coming from Georgia. However, the timber for the 44-gun frigate *Chesapeake,* which had been abandoned in Gosport (Norfolk) was sent to Baltimore. If the moulds and bevels from another ship could be reworked, is it so far fetched to believe that changes could be made in her own design?

Pages 25–26

Here Mr. Chapelle clearly enough tells us that Franklin D. Roosevelt attempted to establish a situation in which a substitution in design was possible! This is hard to believe! And again, of course, F.D.R. is not here to defend himself. "The situation Roosevelt tried to establish . . ." and "It has been pointed out . . . that Roosevelt obviously knew little about Truxtun and his character." . . . "To anyone who has read much about Truxtun, it is impossible to believe. . . ."

It is unfortunate that the *Constellation* Committee, in the 1961 article, used the term "Naval Training Station Museum" in Newport which should have been stated as "Library of Naval War College, U.S. Naval Training Station, Newport, R.I."

It must be stated for the record that we, too, have studied the character of Thomas Truxtun who, although sometimes a bit pompous and officious, was nonetheless—and above all—fair minded. One might just as well reason that the following letter from Stodder could have made him pause to reconsider his position.

I must say to you, Sir, that I have all of my facilities, and for your information I have Mr. Pickering's authority to change the draughts and moulds of this frigate. Mr. Humphreys, I must remind you has had little experience in building other than merchant ships . . . and he being a quaker shoud be catholic [sic] in his design of ships of war. I have been in agreement with the War Office . . . besides even you have disagreed with Humphreys on more than one occasion. I beg you not to write to Humphreys of this matter as Mr. Pickering will tell you he agrees with me as does the brothers here on materials and instructions. I also ask that you act more in the manner befiting a masonic brother and show some amount of trust in your fellows. I am with respect, David Stodder.[27]

Mr. Chapelle attacks the validity of this letter on the grounds that Truxtun would have reacted to it with a "violent explosion of temper, action, and correspondence." It has already been shown that Truxtun was not as explosive as Mr. Chapelle would have us believe. It is also evident from the correspondence herein quoted, that several of Truxtun's letters have been lost and is that so surprising? The possibility exists that he wrote to the Secretary of War on Stodder's changes and that a letter or letters have been lost. As for action, if his letters brought no results, what more could he do?

Mr. Chapelle says that "Any claim that Stodder had Pickering's authority to change the plan would be fiction, for no such grant can be found in the Department papers." The lack of any evidence that such authority was granted does not preclude the authority being granted. According to Mr. Chapelle, if there is no letter existing today stating that an event took place, that event did not take place. This is an absurd position. It has already been established that there was a design change in the frigate *Chesapeake* but no authorization for such a change has been found.

On 18 May 1795, Pickering wrote to Stodder in which he states the following:

I have asked all the builders to communicate with me on new ideas which will benefit the Frigates. Mr. Humphreys may protest, but I assure you I will support your changes in the molds and design.—You are the second person to inform me of Humphreys' protests and I must remind Mr. Humphreys of his status and of the considerations I have given the builders, to improve his ships. I have informed him that you are the owner of a navy-yard and also a master-builder and that your changes as displayed in your model are in accord with Mr. Fox and the War Office. . . ." [28]

Mr. Chapelle attacks this letter on the grounds that all concerned knew that Humphreys owned a shipyard and was a master builder. The letter, of course, does not deny this. It simply states that Stodder was a master builder and the owner of a navy yard. (The phrase "also a master-builder" is ambiguous. It could mean that Stodder like Humphreys was a master-builder.) Mr. Chapelle again demands confirmation. This time confirmation exists. In the official files of the Navy, while it was under the War Department, is a letter dated 20 May 1795 two days after Pickering's letter to Stodder. The communication from the War Department to Humphreys asks him to comment on the enclosed letter from Stodder. Humphreys was asked to comment and it is added that other constructors may also communicate on the improvements of the frigates.[29] Mr. Chapelle does not question this letter.

Page 27

Mr. Chapelle has, for many years, contended that the frame spacing on the "official" plan for *Constellation,* the Humphreys' plan (in reality the Doughty plan) indicates a frame spacing of 26 inches. This ship, with a frame spacing of 32 inches, therefore, cannot have been constructed from that plan! We heartily agree, for that (proposed) plan was never used for the *Constellation!* We invite the attention of the reader to a facsimile of the letter written by David Stodder, the builder, to the Secretary of the Navy dated 30 April 1795 [30] in which he states "The keel is 18 In broad Timber and room [frame spacing] 32 In. . . ." What more basic evidence do we need in determining this dimension? Mr. Chapelle's reaction to this document is astounding! We hear now that *"There is a simple explanation to all this"* (italics mine) for the one man who can tell us what we want to know, Stodder, "made a mistake. . . ."!—a mistake by the shipbuilder in 1795 which just happens to coincide exactly with the dimensions still found on the ship! The reader may recognize the obvious fact that the entire case can rest on this document until Mr. Chapelle can justify the "mistake." Furthermore, when *Constellation* was drydocked in 1964, the keel was carefully measured throughout its length. The average siding was found to vary from 17¼ inches to a full 18 inches, just as David Stodder set down in his letter of 30 April 1795 (Figure 4, Part 3).

Now, we must again consider the "Transverse Sections" dated "Feb. 1853." [31] The confusion occasioned by the various plans and documents is admittedly frustrating and this plan is no exception. The plan appears to be taken directly from the ship as indicated by the offsets outboard of the sections. But was it? Are we to believe the notation of January 1853 in the Delano notebook? "In pencil"—"Underwater body of Constellation does not match drawing of Humphrey Plan or the sketched drawings 1852 showing sections of the hull. This fact was discovered during the docking of the ship to fit her for the blocking to draw her into the shiphouse." Mr. Chapelle's comments on this "diary" are typical of his treatment of Roosevelt's writings. For one thing, Mr. Chapelle appears to be in error as to Benjamin F. Delano who was stationed in New York during 1853. It is true that this writer had made the same error; however, continued research by the *Constellation* Committee and the Navy Department in 1968 revealed that Edward H. Delano, not Benjamin F., was stationed at Norfolk (Gosport) in 1853 and it is his signature that we find on various documents at that station. In one instance, we note the signature, B. F. Delano on the document cited by Mr. Chapelle; however, close examination reveals that the initials appear to have been traced over. In the process, the letters "E.H." appear to have been mistakenly taken for "B.F." If this assumption is correct, the value of that document was all but destroyed by the tampering.

At this moment, we are of course, discussing the Delano notebook which Mr. Chapelle points out has not been produced by the authors of the 1961 article. Of course, the *Constellation* Committee too would like to find the original diary; however, the absence of that prime source, we have to be content with what was we found at the National Archives in Washington, D.C. officially stamped NA–RG 45.[32] While this writer has some reservations concerning this typewritten copy, we have to work with whatever is available. If we cannot get to the truth, we must get as close to it as available information will permit, and that means cool-headed interpretation of much questionable material.

We must agree that some of the language does not appear to fit the time or the place and that some of the nomenclature is of questionable nature; however, several of the terms are not as erroneous as Mr. Chapelle would have us believe· The application of a bit of logical reasoning indicates that "chain iron" is rather close to "chainplates" and what is the definition of "hogging?" Why! *Sagging at the ends!* "Cut to pieces" of course could mean much more than merely "cutting in two" since much more cutting was contemplated, such as the subsequent removal of her entire topside. As for the use of cotton on large ships, my own recollection is that on the wales and bottom planks, for 5-inch thick plank, six double threads of oakum and two single threads of spunyarn were used. On topsides and waterways, five threads black oakum and one thread of white oakum—*or cotton* were used.[33]

While this writer must take exception to such strong terms as "unthinkable" and "impossible to accept," it is agreed that the caulking operation appears to be somewhat early in the sequence of construction.

Returning to the plan of Sections, if they did not match the "underwater body", where did they come from? Mr. Chapelle's analysis of this plan is a good one. We consider this to be the best single effort in his manuscript.

Both parties have now concluded that the sections are taken from the Humphreys-Doughty plan of 1794.

Delano's notes, if we can believe what we read, tell us that the sketches did not match the ship, but further, they did match the Humphreys plan! (To what sketches was Delano referring?)

A careful check of the Gosport Log Book (1853) indicating the work load and dispersal of yard personnel, gives no indication of people assigned to *Constellation* in the month of February for the purpose of erecting scaffolds and preparing the ship for an external take-off of her hull lines. The only reference to staging for the ship comes almost four months later in a letter from Captain Samuel S. Breese, Commanding officer Navy Yard, Gosport to Joseph Smith, Chief, Bureau of Yards and Docks, Washington.[34]

The most persistent question is: Why would it be necessary to take off the lines of a ship which Mr. Chapelle insists were already well established? The existence of the Humphreys-Doughty plan of 1794 should have been all they required!

It is not unheard of to take the lines of a ship from the plan, rather than expend much more labor in the erection of scaffolding and then to send the draftsmen (and a crew would be required) out to the ship in mid-winter to take their measurements; truly an unenviable job.

We must suggest that the take-off was accomplished on the drawing board, scaled from the old plan and found incompatible with the ship. As Mr. Chapelle states, "the sketch of the 32″ frame spacing marked 'old' cannot be accounted for", but of course, it will not go away! (Figure 6.) It must be tied to David Stodder's letter of 30 April 1795.[35] Of course the plan of the keel (C&R Plan 107–13–4A) shows the original hog.[36] As Mr. Chapelle states, this drawing is dated as "*Received January* 1853" (italics mine). Received from where? Incidentally, this plot of the keel, when overlayed on the Lines Plan of the present ship, is compatible from the stern post to the stem and up through the forefoot, and Mr. Chapelle agrees that the plan illustrates the original keel!

Page 30

In referring to deadrise and sharp ends in all the 1794 frigates and most particularly to the *Constellation*, Mr. Chapelle states that "In no captain's correspondence is there mention of a remarkably sharp entrance. . . ." This, of course, is not true if we are to take into account Truxtun's letter to Livingston date 22 May 1798,[37] which states "Stodder's new ideas on the form of the bow will no doubt increase her speed through the water". Mr. Chapelle's statement concerning the fact that *Constellation*'s bow was not as sharp as many other vessels built at Baltimore could be

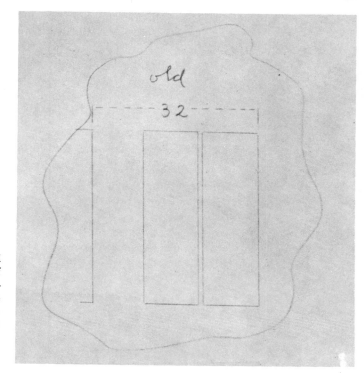

FIGURE 6.—Sketch found on transverse sections of frigate *Constellation,* Norfolk, 1853, from Figure 5 of Part 1 (National Archives, 107–13–4B). Note 32-inch frame spacing.

somewhat misleading. Aside from the fact that the shape of the bow has been rather thoroughly covered in previous pages, the vessels he now compares with the *Constellation* are either much smaller bay and coastal vessels or as he says—"Baltimore Clippers"—a design of much later date.

Page 31

Mr. Fox, in his statement of services, 27 November 1826, stated that the live oak previously prepared at Norfolk for that now abandoned project "had been taken to finish the frigate Constellation." Mr. Chapelle refers to the Norfolk ship as a 36-gun frigate whereas she was in reality a small 44 on the original listing as indicated by "Ships of War draughted by Josiah Fox," dated 27 November 1826, "near Wheeling, Va."—"Frigates of 44 Guns [sic]".[38]

Further to the interesting question of shifting timbers from one ship project to another, we submit the following sequence of events taken from the correspondence on Naval Affairs when the Navy was under the War Department.[39] It will be seen that timbers *were* exchanged, even between 36-gun ships and 44s.

To Joshua Humphreys—Philadelphia—War Office September 6, 1796. Sir Be pleased to deliver to Mr. George Claghorne all such pieces of timber as may not be wanted for the completing the frigate now building by you; the pieces promised to be sent to Baltimore excepted.[40]

On page 105 of the War Office correspondence—Four letters from the War Department in 1796 transferring timbers from Philadelphia to Baltimore, Philadelphia to Boston, Norfolk to Boston, Norfolk to Baltimore, and Baltimore to Boston. We note also the following which explains the difficulty of procuring live oak for all six frigates.

War Office, June 29, 1795, to Tench Francis, Esquire. Had the difficult[ties] of getting the live oak been foreseen—had it been known that full and regular supplies for two [ships] only, could be kept up—certainly, the carrying forward of six frigates at the same time, would not have been attempted. What should not have been begun, ought now that the facts are known, to be laid aside. Consequently I shall direct four of the Constructors to suspend their labours, . . . or to dismiss all their hands for whom they cannot find constant, and useful employment.[41]

In scanning the old letter book we find another interesting note on the difficulty of procuring the live oak—even from the Savannah River in Georgia. This time it is the stem which is involved (Figure 7). It was David Stodder in Baltimore who sent the

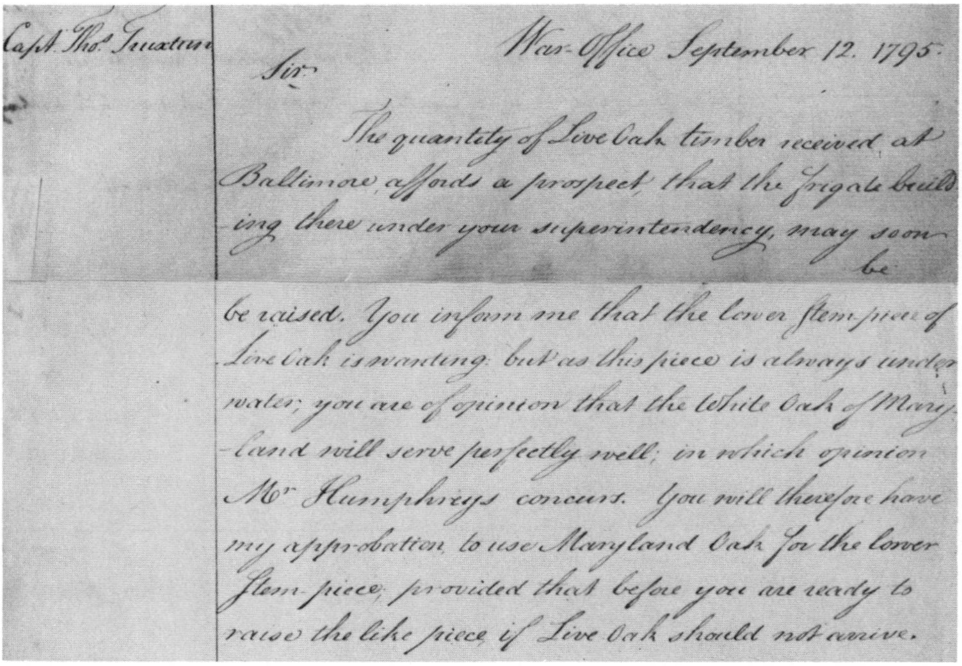
Capt. Thos. Truxtun

War-Office September 12. 1795.

Sir.

The quantity of Live Oak timber received at Baltimore, affords a prospect, that the frigate building there under your superintendency, may soon be be raised. You inform me that the lower Stem-piece of Live Oak is wanting: but as this piece is always under water; you are of opinion that the White Oak of Maryland will serve perfectly well; in which opinion Mr Humphreys concurs. You will therefore have my approbation, to use Maryland Oak for the lower Stem-piece, provided that before you are ready to raise the like piece of Live Oak should not arrive.

FIGURE 7.—Letter from War Office to Thomas Truxtun, 12 September 1795 (National Archives, Washington, D.C., Record Group 45, Entry 374, Letters sent concerning Naval matters, October 1790–June 1798).

The quantity of Live Oak timber received at Baltimore, affords a prospect, that the frigate building there under your superintendency, may soon be raised. You inform me that the lower Stem-piece of Live Oak is wanting: but as this piece is always under water, you are of opinion that the White Oak of Maryland will serve perfectly well; in which opinion Mr. Humphreys concurs. You will therefore have my approbation, to use Maryland Oak for the lower Stem-piece, provided that before you are ready to raise the like piece of Live Oak should not arrive.

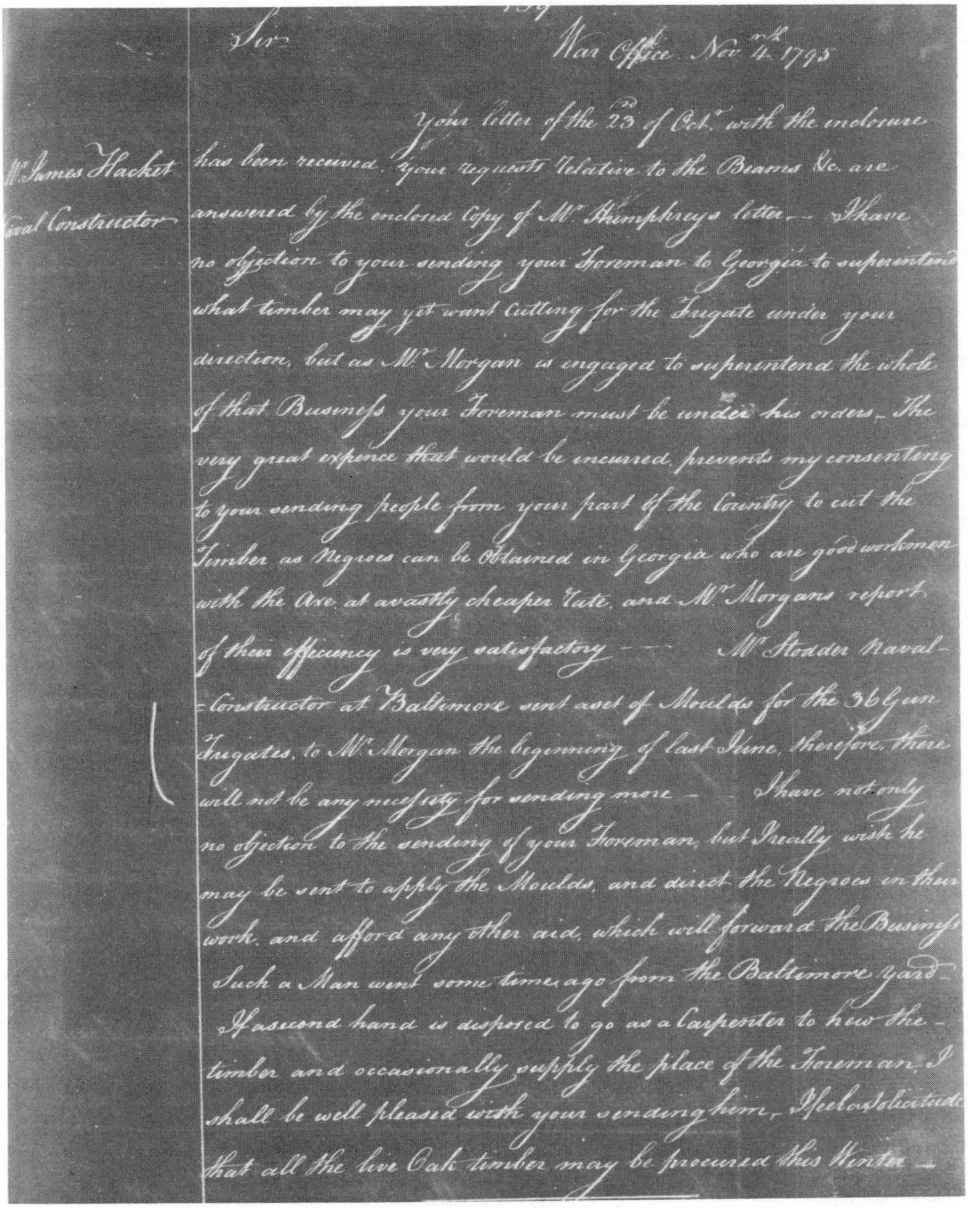

159

Sir War Office Nov.th 4. 1795

Mr. James Hacket
Naval Constructor

Your letter of the 23d of Octr. with the enclosure
has been received. your requests relative to the Beams &c. are
answered by the enclosed Copy of Mr. Humphreys letter— I have
no objection to your sending your Foreman to Georgia to superintend
what timber may yet want Cutting for the Frigate under your
direction, but as Mr. Morgan is engaged to superintend the whole
of that Business your Foreman must be under his orders— The
very great expence that would be incurred, prevents my consenting
to your sending people from your part of the Country to cut the
Timber as Negroes can be Obtained in Georgia who are good workmen
with the Axe at a vastly cheaper rate, and Mr. Morgans report
of their efficiency is very satisfactory —— Mr. Stodder Naval-
Constructor at Baltimore sent aset of Moulds for the 36 Gun
Frigates, to Mr. Morgan the beginning of last June, therefore, there
will not be any necessity for sending more— I have not only
no objection to the sending of your Foreman, but I really wish he
may be sent to apply the Moulds, and direct the Negroes in their
work, and afford any other aid, which will forward the Business
Such a Man went some time ago from the Baltimore yard—
If a second hand is disposed to go as a Carpenter to hew the
timber and occasionally supply the place of the Foreman, I
shall be well pleased with your sending him— I feel a solicitude
that all the live Oak timber may be procured this Winter—

FIGURE 8.—Letter from War Office to James Hacket, 4 November 1785 (National Archives, Washington, D.C., Record Group 45, Entry 374, Letters sent concerning Naval matters, October 1790–June 1798).

Mr. Stodder Naval-Constructor at Baltimore sent aset [sic] of Moulds for the 36 Gun Frigates, to Mr. Morgan the beginning of last June, therefore, there will not be any necessity for sending more.

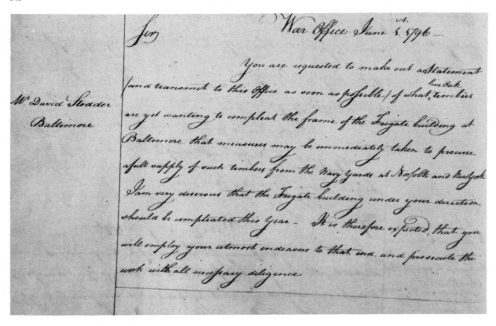

FIGURE 9.—Letter from War Office to David Stodder, 1 June 1796 (National Archives, Washington, D.C., Record Group 45, Entry 374, Letters sent concerning Naval matters, October 1790–June 1798).

You are requested to make out a Statement . . . of what live Oak timbers are yet wanting . . . that measures may be . . . taken to procure a full supply of such timbers from the Navy Yards at Norfolk and New York.

FIGURE 10.—Letter from War Office to John Blagge, 11 June 1796 (National Archives, Washington, D.C., Record Group 45, Entry 374, Letters sent concerning Naval matters, October 1790–June 1798).

You will be pleased to deliver such of the live timbers as may be in the Navy Yard at New York to Messrs Samuel and Joseph Sterret [sic] Naval Agents at Baltimore. . .

moulds for the 36-gun frigates to John Morgan in Georgia. Figures 8–10 further illustrate necessary procurement arrangements of timber.

Page 33

Mr. Chapelle notes that Fox claims credit for draughting the *United States* and *Constellation* and "nowhere mentions Stodder, nor his draught . . . . " The more interesting and unstated remark would include the fact that *Fox supplied a corrected draught,* thus perhaps now claiming the credit for himself. Whatever the scope of those corrections, aside from the placement of the beams and the pumps, the Fox draught becomes the latest actual working plan and the Humphreys' plan becomes obsolete! At this moment, we know nothing of a draught by David Stodder, whether he made one or not—and neither does Mr. Chapelle; and we are not really concerned with the claims of Josiah Fox on any but this ship.

From the Correspondence on Naval Affairs [42] we submit two key letters; one indicating delivery of the Humphreys-Doughty plan to Baltimore (Figure 11) and the other indicating Fox's involvement in the draughts of the ship (Figure 12). This may well bear upon the source of his claim to have "draughted the *Constellation.*" Even so, his plan is referred to as the "corrected draught."

To avoid misleading the reader, it is pointed out that the letter (Figure 12) directed to Thomas Truxtun refers to a "draught . . . which accompanies this [letter, which] is not complete;" and "a more correct draught [is] to be made and transmitted." We have found so far no record of the actual delivery of that draught; however, it is obvious that at least one other draught existed.[43]

It is pointed out at this time that submittal of a preliminary plan does not now and never did constitute a guarantee that further development in the form of radical alterations could not occur in the designs nor is there any guarantee that the original plan will be used at all! As to the statement of Captain Tingey in 1811 referring to a "flat transom," Mr. Chapelle tells us that this is the "first and apparently the only reference to a peculiar transom on this ship; no other reference to an unusual transom has yet been found." From this, we are to gather that because he has seen no other reference, that there is no other and we must conclude that the statement is false.

FIGURE 11.—Letter from War Department to Samuel and Joseph Sterrett, 18 February 1795 (National Archives, Washington, D.C., Record Group 45, Entry 374, Letters sent concerning Naval matters, October 1790–June 1798).

Herewith you will receive in a Tin case the draught of the Frigate to be built at Baltimore; prepared under the direction of Mr. Humphreys, the Constructor at this port. . . .

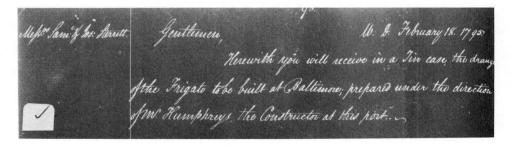

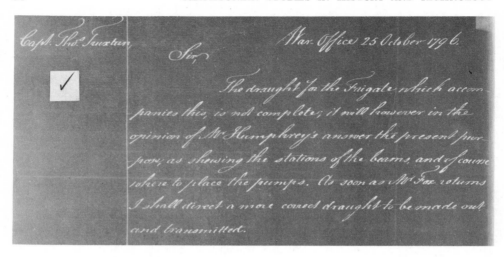

FIGURE 12.—Letter from War Office to Thomas Truxtun, 25 October 1796 (National Archives, Washington, D.C., Record Group 45, Entry 374, Letters sent concerning Naval matters, October 1790–June 1798).

The draught for the Frigate which accompanies this, is not complete; it will . . . in the opinion of Mr. Humphrey's answer the present purpose, as shewing [sic] the stations of the beams and . . . where to place the pumps. As soon as Mr. Fox returns I shall direct a more correct draught to be made out and transmitted.

Again, Mr. Chapelle finds "No office file copy . . . in the Navy Department records," of the Capps Report. In consideration of that statement, the reader is no doubt asked to conclude that this copy is a hoax. We think it would have been closer to the truth if he had added that it too was found by this commitee in Newport (File 1231–A)[44] in 1960 and is still there—unless, as we have heard before, someone has tampered with the files. We shall have more to say about "missing" Archive documents in later pages.

Mr. Chapelle has several times stated that *Constellation*'s stern was rounded in 1853–55. The Samuel Humphrey statement here referred to infers that plans were afoot to round the stern—and as can be seen in Figure 20, there is convincing evidence that this alteration actually occurred in 1829 and not in 1853 as Mr. Chapelle would have us believe. Another point of confusion is added by the change in beam in 1812 which Mr. Chapelle says could not have occurred unless a very extensive alteration had been made—involving all frames from the turn of the bilge to the rail, ceiling, planking, knees shelf strakes, etc. Nowhere in footnote 29 (pages 25–26) of the 1961 article did the *Constellation* Committee even infer that the "moulded *beam*" was altered, only that "It is not possible to reconcile the several figures given in the early records for the *Constellation*'s beam, nor can it be clearly ascertained what each writer meant by the different terms used." Often, the early records indicate "extreme beam", "beam amidships", "moulded beam" or simply "beam."

The "extreme beam" is, of course, the widest dimension of the hull from the outside of plank on one side to the outside of plank on the opposite side. "Beam amidships" is the athwartship dimension at the longitudinal midsection of the hull. "Generally" this dimension is measured from *outside of the frame* on one side *to outside of frame opposite*. The *widest section* of the hull may also be designated as the midship section by the designers, whether it happens to fall at the longitudinal midsection or at another station of the hull. This too may be the section for measuring the beam, if the designer or builder so indicates. The "moulded beam" is the dimension measured from outside of frame to outside of frame opposite. To complicate matters even further, this writer has often heard it said that "moulded beam" is measured on *steel ships* from outer surface of the steel frame to outer surface of the frame opposite, while on wood ships the same term is used for the dimension from outer surface of plank to outer surface of plank opposite. Even this does not always hold true. Note that the body plan is drawn to outside of the frames (Figures 1 and 10 of Part 3).Our conclusion was finally based on the builders or designers designation for the moulded beam—and all too often the early records do not reveal his initial intent.

As the reader can see, the term "beam" can indicate a variety of dimensions and the *Constellation* Committee in 1961 only used that generic term to point out the confusion in the interpretation of the old documents.

Page 37

Mr. Chapelle here introduces a Newspaper account of 11 July 1853 which stated that the " 'Old Constellation' was literally torn to pieces preparatory to the building of a new Constellation," and that the massive keel was "placed in one of the ship houses" (Daily Southern Argus, Norfolk, Virginia).

The literal interpretation of "torn to pieces" is somewhat open to question. A graphic example is seen in Figure 13 of the same ship, "torn to pieces" preparatory to the building of a new *Constellation*. The date? *January 1968*. The photo shows the gun deck and spar deck levels, "torn to pieces." We cannot pretend that the work here was as extensive as of the 1853 rebuilding but even so, the result of the work here again produced a "new" *Constellation*. It is as always, a figure of speech as old as our language.

Further, the newspaper article of 11 July 1853 states that "her massive keel" was "placed in a ship house." This is certainly true, as we know that she was placed in shiphouse "B" at Gosport where the operation was performed.[45] We must not miss the fact that the keel of the old ship was placed in that shiphouse and secondly that the author is impressed with the massive nature of the keel. This immediately suggests that the floor timbers, at the very least, are still attached to that keel—and this in itself could constitute perpetuation of the old ship!

To illustrate the hazards encountered in the quoting of newspaper articles, we submit the following report as published in *The Philadelphia Saturday Inquirer,* 19 July 1845. According to this account (Figure 14), this preposterous article also appeared in the *Baltimore Patriot* as well as the *Norfolk Herald*. The *Constellation,* of course, was never altered to include steam propulsion, although such proposals were submitted to the Navy Department. Correspondence in the National Archives

FIGURE 13.—Gun Deck and Quarter Deck of the *Constellation,*
January 1968 at Pier 7, Baltimore.

(Record Group 45, Bureau Letters) dated 8 and 11 July 1845 proposed that the *Constellation* as well as the *Macedonian* be converted to steam propulsion. There is no evidence, however, of actual "orders" ever having been received at Gosport to proceed with such a project, much less to "proceed immediately." It is interesting to note that the article is dated 10 July, which fits neatly within the dates of the above-mentioned correspondence of 8 and 11 July. It would appear that someone in a fit of hopeful anticipation had let the story "leak out."

As we are well aware, the *Constellation* was never increased by "thirty feet" to a total of 200 feet between perpendiculars. Such an increase could not have resulted in a 200-foot ship, neither overall nor between perpendiculars. We note also that the author of this article believed the ship to have been built in Baltimore. In 1845?

The Restoration Committee has had several sad experiences with inaccurate reporting by the modern press. We are now asked by Mr. Chapelle to note without question newspaper accounts well over a century old, written and edited under comparatively archaic conditions of communication in comparison with the technological advantages now seemingly enjoyed by our press, radio, and television reporters.

This writer does not intend to become a party to the memo to Commanding Officer of the Point dated May 1918. This office hardly feels the need to depend upon such highly questionable material, but the alleged extent of Mr. Chapelle's

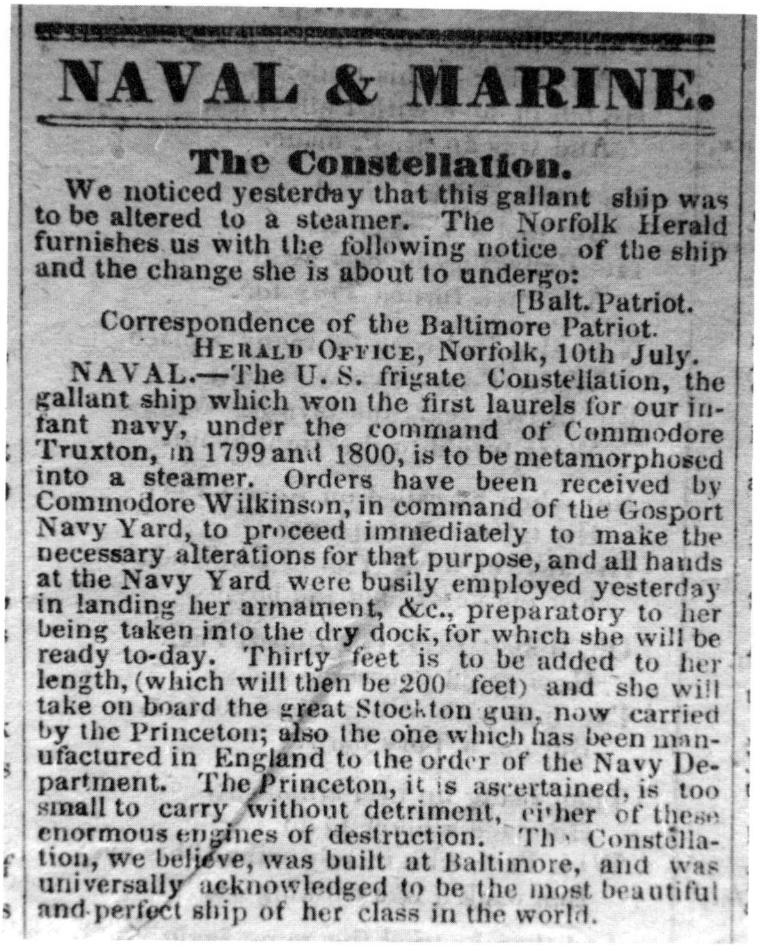

NAVAL & MARINE.

The Constellation.

We noticed yesterday that this gallant ship was to be altered to a steamer. The Norfolk Herald furnishes us with the following notice of the ship and the change she is about to undergo:

[Balt. Patriot.

Correspondence of the Baltimore Patriot.

HERALD OFFICE, Norfolk, 10th July.

NAVAL.—The U. S. frigate Constellation, the gallant ship which won the first laurels for our infant navy, under the command of Commodore Truxton, in 1799 and 1800, is to be metamorphosed into a steamer. Orders have been received by Commodore Wilkinson, in command of the Gosport Navy Yard, to proceed immediately to make the necessary alterations for that purpose, and all hands at the Navy Yard were busily employed yesterday in landing her armament, &c., preparatory to her being taken into the dry dock, for which she will be ready to-day. Thirty feet is to be added to her length, (which will then be 200 feet) and she will take on board the great Stockton gun, now carried by the Princeton; also the one which has been manufactured in England to the order of the Navy Department. The Princeton, it is ascertained, is too small to carry without detriment, either of these enormous engines of destruction. The Constellation, we believe, was built at Baltimore, and was universally acknowledged to be the most beautiful and perfect ship of her class in the world.

FIGURE 14.—Article from the *Philadelphia Saturday Enquirer,* 10 July 1845.

"investigation" is remarkable. On one line, Mr. Chapelle tells us that "the designation" U.S. Frigate *Constellation*" was used in a few instances (actually the ship was almost always referred to as a frigate) and a few lines later suggests that the " 'Commanding Officer of the Point' was clairvoyant" in using that designation, as he should have waited for Mr. Roosevelt to say it first.

Page 37

Mr. Chapelle asks us to consider the record of rebuilt naval vessels listed in his Historical Notes as if that were the official record of Naval Construction. We must reiterate that we have already denounced as invalid to the current question that which has happened to another or other ships; and let us not forget that the Navy has never denied the records of those ships.

Mr. Chapelle inadvertently points out his own published errors in stating that *Constellation* was destroyed in 1852.[46] It is of course, a well established fact that the frigate was not hauled until 23 February 1853 in order that the work could begin.

Pages 38–40

The paper which Mr. Chapelle here attempts to discredit appears to be nothing more than a summary, transcribed sometime after 1950 *and no one has ever denied the fact!* There is no indication of a claim that this "document" of insignificant proportions was written for any purpose other than as a memorandum or as a reminder to the transcriber. Indications point to the conclusion that it may have been transcribed from an original memo. The rough notes in the files of the Committee bear our comment, "so what?"

Pages 43–44

Mr. Chapelle wastes little time or space in an initial attempt to discredit this writer and the work presented to the Society of Naval Architects and Marine Engineers on 7 May 1966. His suggestion that this office attempts to "impeach" the Congressional papers, Navy records, etc. is, of course, untrue.

Mr. Chapelle's treatment of the mould loft offsets and Lenthall's lines plan of June 1853 appears to be somewhat shortsighted and in any case the single paragraph he presents is oversimplified though filled with lengthy terminology, which we would suppose to be more appropriately listed in a bibliography than employed in the body of his work.

Regarding the several documents listing this ship as the "New *Constellation*." It is not at all unusual to refer to a newly reconstructed ship as the "new" model. This certainly simplifies identification of the ship and points up the fact of reconstruction. The Lenthall plan indicated here by Mr. Chapelle is not the only one bearing the "New" title—although that line is an addition *in pencil*. An even more revealing plan of the "new" and "old" *Constellation* is discussed on page 126—as well as the structure of the drawing here noted by Mr. Chapelle as C&R 28–3–5 dated June 1853 by John Lenthall (p. 89).

The 1853 mould loft offsets reflect a different design than that indicated in Humphrey's plan. If this theory is correct and we assume her official draughts were destroyed in the Washington Navy Yard in 1814 (or else where are they) that leaves this ship, among others perhaps, without many of her original plans so important in determining the contours of her underbody. If that were not true, then why the need now to *take the lines* from the hull and to lay down these lines on the mould loft floor? It would seem reasonable to assume that here was an opportunity to lay down the complete "new" ship including the 12-foot extension and any other alterations to her moulded lines. These offsets when translated into a draught, form the plan of John Lenthall, June 1853 (Figure 15).

FIGURE 15.—Lines plan of Sloop of War *Constellation* by John Lenthall, June 1853 (National Archives, Washington, D.C., Record Group 19, C&R Plan 28–3–5).

Sloop of War Constellation

scale 5

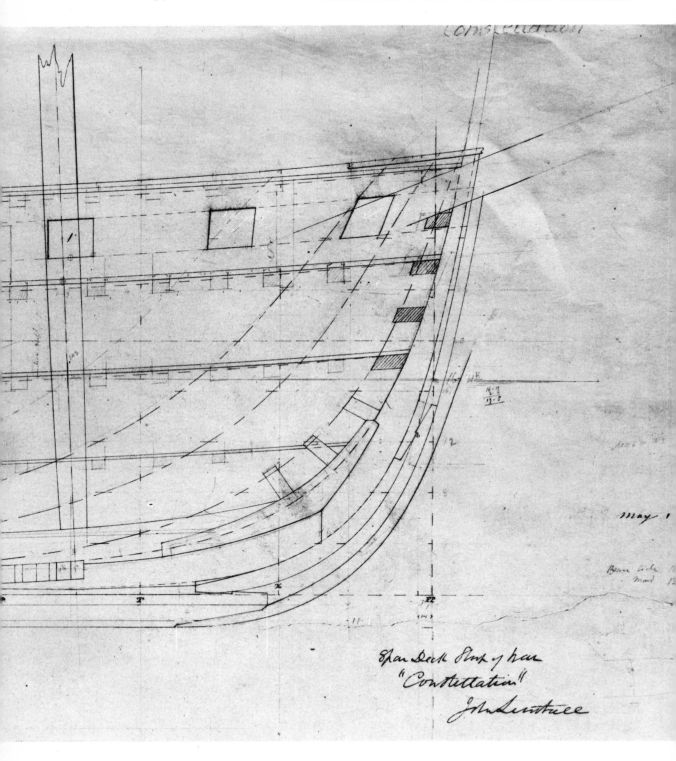

Spar Deck Plan of the
"Constellation"

John Lenthall

FIGURE 16.—Lines plan of Sloop of War *Constellation* by John Lenthall, May 1853 (Lenthall Documents Collection, Franklin Institute, Philadelphia, Pennsylvania).

Mr. Chapelle says "There is no evidence . . . that the Lenthall draught and the offsets of 1853 were take-offs of any old vessel; . . ." In truth we don't know exactly what happened—and neither does he!

There is more to the June 1853 C&R plan than Mr. Chapelle has noted. This drawing can be traced to an original dated *May 1853* (Figure 16), indicating some of the structural elements of the hull. Among the details shown are the original breast hooks in way of the apron of the stem. Lenthall shows the "new" hooks in the upper works as "hatched in" while the "old" (original) timbers are not thus shaded showing the very obvious difference in old and new structure (see page 90).

This writer appears to have "admitted" (in his 1966 paper) that "the corvette was obviously 'represented' in John Lenthall's plan"! I'm not quite sure of Mr. Chapelle's meaning but I seem to have been guilty of stating a fact that up to this point I thought we both agreed upon.

In commenting upon the "F.D.R." notation and the vertical line on the Lenthall plan fragment, Mr. Chapelle tells us that it "merely shows the ignorance of the person who drew the vertical line. Station F is well forward of ⊕ [amidships] . . . and the cutting-in-two, . . . would have had to have been made at ⊕ (dead flat station). . . ." If the reader will reflect a moment on this statement, which is so neatly wrapped in illogical phraseology, he will note that the inscription says "new, 12′ *aft*" (of frame F). If we were now to delete the "new" 12-foot section and move the remaining (original) forward section aft to close the gap, where would frame F

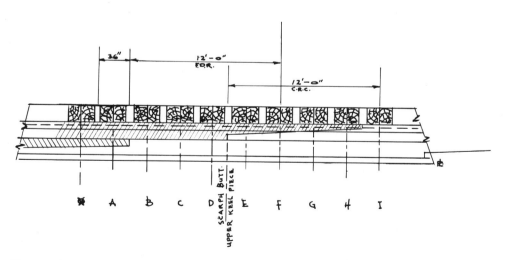

FIGURE 17.—Diagram of the Roosevelt theory and the committee's findings on the lengthened section. F.D.R. theory embraces frames B, C, D, E and after sister of "F" overlapping CRC's findings, E, F, G, H and after sister of I.

lie now? Frames B, C, D and E are new, and frame F would be in the room now occupied by B, only 36 inches from the amidships frame station and the dead flat! (Figure 17) In any case, the 4½ frames when applied as a multiple of the 32" spacing equals 12.015 feet. This is certainly more than a coincidence. The original length of the ship, 164.0 feet plus the 12-foot extension is exactly 176.0 feet, the present length. The 26 inch frame spacing indicated on the Humphreys-Doughty plan cannot be applied as a multiple arriving at 12.0 feet. Note also—measuring 12 feet aft of frame I, we arrive at the butt end of the top keel piece, making it possible to retain the timber abaft the cut while installing a new 40-foot timber forward and another below (Figure 17).

Page 45

We will not again use time and space belaboring the Fox "Sworn Statement." As for the "time and effort [which] would have been avoided if [this] Committee had studied the history of American naval shipbuilding. . . ." we have long since become conditioned to Mr. Chapelle's critical phraseology.

"No indication has been found that Stodder was more than a practical merchant-ship builder." This hardly deserves comment, as we have shown several indications that Stodder deserves a better fate than Mr. Chapelle would assign him. Mr. Chapelle states that "Some comments in Mr. Polland's paper . . . show that he, too, though a naval architect, was unacquainted with wooden shipbuilding. . . ." Although mistakes may have been made on both sides of this very interesting affair, Mr. Chapelle may one day find that throughout his attacks on this office, he has committed the unforgiveable blunder of underestimating his opponents! He now seeks to convince the reader by lightly passing off our observations as being those of one "unacquainted with wooden shipbuilding". After 10 years as Technical Advisor on this project, after many surveys of the *Constitution* in Boston and the *Morgan* in Mystic, as director of International Sail, An Association of Restored Sailing Ships and lately involved in the expansion of this country's new fishing fleet, many of which are of wood construction (and surprisingly similar in hull construction detail to ships built in the past two centuries), I hardly feel as one unacquainted with wooden shipbuilding.

Mr. Chapelle is speaking now of my statement concerning the obvious "*hand hewn timbers*" which we have placed in comparison with adjacent circular saw-cut timber. It is becoming more apparent that he does not, or does not wish to, follow the intended description which we must now admit should have been elaborated upon for the layman (Figure 18).

The frames on either side of E, F, G, and H are obviously adz cut as the tool marks are easily distinguishable and the number of bolt holes, together with the color and texture of the wood, bears testimony to the fact that they are of greater age in the ship than the four saw-cut frames E, F, G and H. Many of the bolt holes are elongated and some doubled. The earlier frames are overwhelmingly evident as far aft as number 28. Mr. Chapelle neglects to say, of course, that we observe the rotary marks only *on the sidings* of the frames and that the adjacent frames are adz cut *on all four sides,* the mouldings as well as the sidings. To attempt to run the curved or shaped-and-beveled side of a large timber through a mill saw would be impractical and is, indeed, unheard of. The sidings, however, are all straight cuts, easily made in the mill or yard.

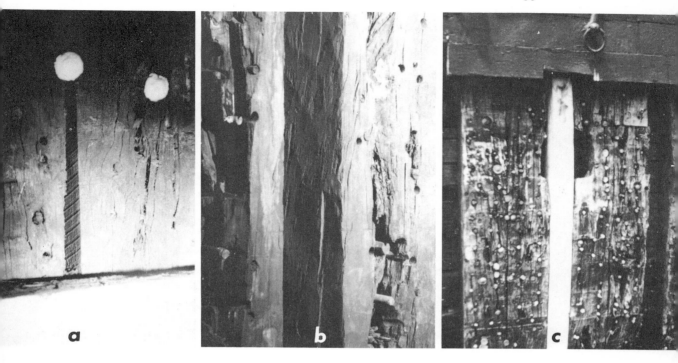

FIGURE 18.—Framing timbers from the *Constellation:* a, saw mill cut; b, adz cut; c, typical framing.

FIGURE 19.—A typical framing timber.

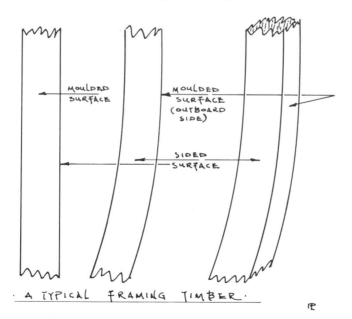

Upon examination of the sketch, Figure 19, one may readily determine the advantage in employing a power driven circular mill saw on the sidings of the various framing timbers E, F, G, H, and the lengthened section. It should be quite obvious that we are speaking now of a single straight cut from top to bottom of the futtock. These same timbers are certainly trimmed to final shape on the moulded or outer surfaces by using the adz. In comparison, it was pointed out that the earlier timbers adjacent to the lengthened section are entirely adz cut on the sidings as well as on the moulded surfaces. We have *not,* as Mr. Chapelle would have the reader believe, implied "that hand-hewn timbers were an acceptable evidence of great age," unless a comparison is available. The conclusion is certainly justified by results of that comparison.

Page 45

This writer's statement on page 17 of his 1966 report [47] concerning *Constellation's* peculiar rolling characteristics and Tingey's alteration to the tumblehome earns Mr. Chapelle's announcement that "the tumble home, in the American frigates *whose plans exist,* was quite small . . . ." We have stated often enough that the plans for this ship—if they exist at all, are certainly unknown to us. His rather curious statement that the tumblehome in those ships was "quite small at main or gun deck level and marked only as the main rail was approached," pictures a sudden change in the sectional curve above the spar deck amidships allowing only about 4 feet of height for the marked tumblehome. Not a very pretty picture.

Mr. Chapelle chooses to take issue with Thomas Truxtun who stated *Constellation* was one of the fastest ships afloat.[48] The truth of the matter is that we are not really concerned here with whether she was fast or not. That is not the issue, although such reference did appear in the 1966 S.N.A.M.E. paper within the context of Truxtun's letter to Ben Stoddert, Secretary of the Navy, dated August 1798.[49] Mr. Chapelle finds it difficult to interpret the transcribers evaluation of *"renew rot in timbers. . . ."* in "Another version of the Tingey report of 1812–13. . . ." While this writer cannot claim any degree of clairvoyance, it somehow was not too difficult to piece the words together resulting in ". . . to renew *rotten* timbers . . .," which certainly makes more sense. Mr. Chapelle is correct in finally determining that "Tingey hardly intended to 'renew rot' in timbers."

Mr. Chapelle makes "a rather curious statement" in reference to the frigate's reputation for "lack of stiffness," a very, very unprofessional appraisal for a vessel which may lack initial stability. Such a vessel is generally referred to as "cranky" by naval architects, shipbuilders, seamen, and admirals.

Page 48

In reviewing Mr. Chapelle's work, we arrive at a most interesting side project which naturally enough Mr. Chapelle discredits, discounts, and finally dismisses—but again—it will not go away! Mr. Chapelle, as early as 1949, claimed in the *Providence Sunday Journal* (3 April 1949) that the "new ship launched in 1855, was round-sterned and originally had but one deck above the waterline, making her . . . a flush decked sloop-of-war."

In following pages, we will briefly discuss a plan indicating a survey of the mizzen mast, dated 1840. The plan is properly and clearly marked "Constellation" and "1840." A most interesting observation is the obvious similarity of the stern profile to that of the ship as it appears today. *It shows the rounded stern* which Mr. Chapelle claims was constructed in 1853–55. We further stated in our paper [50] that a minutely inscribed date just above the waterline reveals that the plan may have originated in 1829 (Figure 20). Our first impression of this drawing (actually a segment of a rigging plan) led us to question the fact that it was drawn in reverse; that is, the ship is drawn with the *stern* on the right side—while the normal orientation of a draught always indicates the bow on the right side unless circumstances dictate otherwise.

Why would a draught be superimposed on the reverse side? As often occurs, a sketch of minor or temporary nature is easily overlayed on a detailed draught by using the reverse side. As in this case, when the survey of the mizzen mast was complete, the plan was turned back on its original side. Mr. Chapelle, commenting on this Mizzen Mast Survey, states, "This is said to be in National Archives 'RG–45,' but the Archives staff have not been able to find it, with only this available reference." He does not note, however, whether it was found or not, only that it could not be found with that reference. In any case, this office has in its files the official National Archives photostat copy, herein reproduced as Figure 20.[51] (See also Figure 5a, Part 3.)

Concerning various Archives files, this writer has had the occasion to order reprints of documents only to find that the originals have been misfiled or otherwise misplaced. Many of our older institutions have found it understandably necessary to follow archaic filing systems established many years ago due to the expense involved in change-over to modern methods. We cannot help wondering, however, at the memorable coincidence that there are now three plans missing from the files of the National Archives (RG–45, Entry 464, AS Subject Files) since the fall of 1968. Photostatic reproductions of all three are in the files of this committee!

Page 49

Mr. Chapelle attempts to discredit the "Capps Report," found in Newport and presented in its original form, without corrections, in the 1966 S.N.A.M.E. paper, by this writer. We shall make no excuses for any unprofessional language contained in that report. As we have already stated, shipbuilding nomenclature or for that matter, the language of any technical field is understandably difficult for a layman to transliterate and transcribe. This observation is based upon long experience with helpful and sometimes not so helpful research teams.

Here Mr. Chapelle's familiar theme rings out! "There is no evidence that . . ." or "There is nothing of this sort in his papers . . .", etc.

Page 50

Some comments in Mr. Chapelle's manuscript show that he, while a Naval Historian, is somewhat unacquainted with practical shipbuilding. "Why the ship required so much repair below the bilge (which normally outlives the topside in a wooden hull) and so little in the topsides is not stated." His objections to the replacement of four and then again fourteen more third futtocks is not borne out by *Con-*

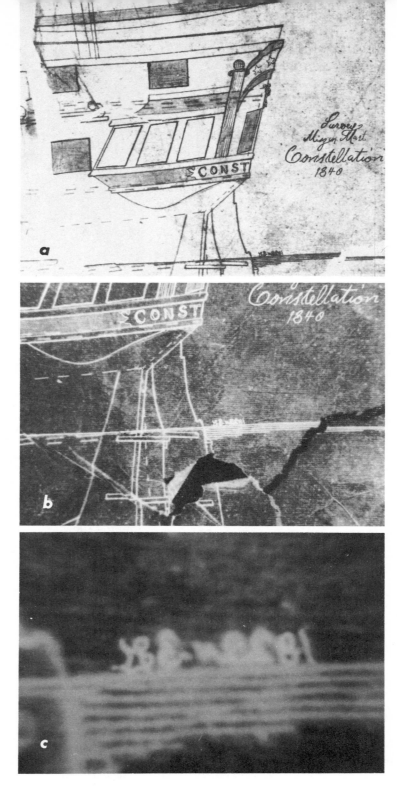

FIGURE 20.—Magnification of 1829 date on the Mizzen Mast Survey 1840 (National Archives, Washington, D.C., Record Group 45, Entry 374).

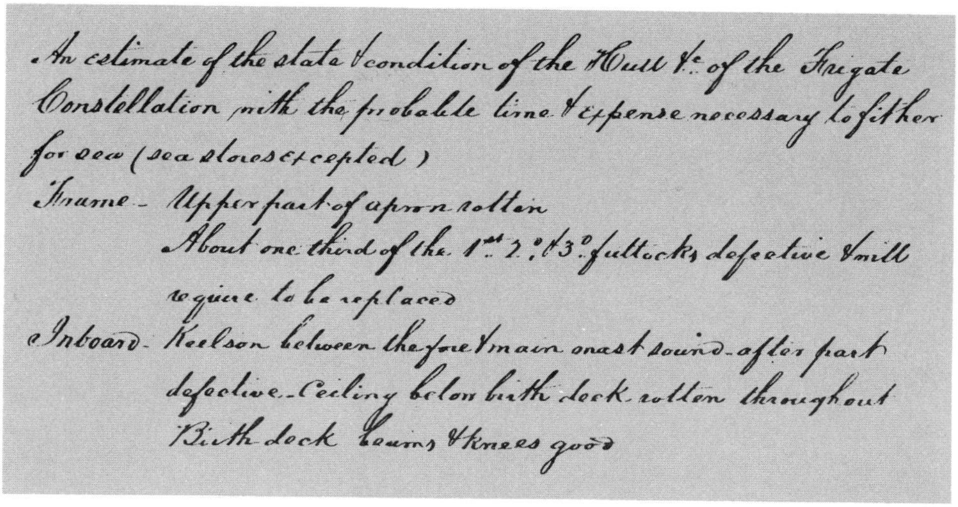

An estimate of the state & condition of the Hull &c. of the Frigate
Constellation with the probable time & expense necessary to fit her
for sea (sea stores excepted)
Frame - Upper part of apron rotten
About one third of the 1st 2d & 3d futtocks defective & will
require to be replaced
Inboard - Keelson between the fore & main mast sound - after part
defective - Ceiling below birth deck rotten throughout
Birth deck beams & knees good

FIGURE 21.—Estimate of state and condition of the *Constellation* indicating extensive repairs to the first, second, and third futtocks (Files of *Constellation* Restoration Committee, Baltimore, Maryland).

stellation's contemporary reports on repair (Figure 21), "An Estimate of the state & condition of the Hull, etc. of the Frigate Constellation . . . ," circa-1840, "Upper part of apron rotten. About *one third of the 1st, 2nd and 3rd futtocks defective & will require to be replaced* . . ." (italics mine).

While we agree that wooden ships generally deteriorate first between wind and water (or between the waterline and the rail) due to, of course, the intermittent spraying and drying of the sides; we must also take into account that, depending upon various conditions, the lower futtocks also are subject to decay. At any rate, Mr. Chapelle's statement fails to stand on its own feet in light of the "Estimate."

Mr. Chapelle makes reference to the "incorrect nomenclature" of the Capps Report in which the *3rd* futtocks are "spliced." His attempt to build a case again based on the employment of language is somewhat erroneous and may mislead the reader. "Futtocks" he says, "were usually 'butted' and not scarphed, by the way."

As the frames here are "sistered" or doubled, that is, two 12-inch timbers are edge bolted together thus forming a frame doubling the sectional area of a single timber (and the butts well shifted, of course), we must insist that the replacement of a single timber or futtock within the structure of the built-up frame constitutes a *splice*. All this does not prove much, of course, except that even Mr. Chapelle can be wrong!

Another statement of Mr. Chapelle's that framing timbers were usually butted together—not scarphed, cannot go unchallenged. Of course, he gives no source material, leaving the reader no choice but to rely on his (Chapelle's) recollection.

Unfortunately, we again cannot agree—and with good reason, for the proof is here, not buried in the archives of a library but now exposed to view for all to see. It is only necessary, of course, to correctly interpret what we see, and the answer can be elusive!

A survey of the floor-to-futtock connections in *Constellation's* amidships area reveals the arrangement of timbers as indicated here in the midship section plan (Figure 14, Part 3). Many of the frames cut down to the floor timbers in 1853–55, were cut through existing anchor joints which in themselves constitute a scarphed timber.

Here again, it appears that Mr. Chapelle wages a battle against a structure which he could never have seen. The floors were not open to view for many years until the present restoration was well under way.

In cutting down the frames, in order to keep the short arm of the floor timber as long as possible, it was cut off through the center of the anchor piece, at the extreme end of the floor. The anchor piece, in the process, was cut in two and one triangular half was bolted back to the end of the floor timber in order to provide a solid square butt for the connection to the new first futtock; so we see that either system could have been used and in fact, both systems for connecting the timbers were employed here.

The rebuilt joint shows on the elevation of the midship section plan, as a triangular shape at the end of the short arm scarphed to the floor! This is the case on every frame except those within the new 12-foot section.

Further to the scarphing of framing timbers versus "butt" connections, we make reference to the official plans of HMS *Victory*, H.M. Dockyard, Portsmouth. Here the scarphed joints and anchor pieces are all too obvious to deny in this discussion.

This writer has several times surveyed the *Constitution* in Boston Harbor. The main hold is filled by the stones and blocks of old Boston streets comprising the ballast. This made it impossible to view the floors and first futtocks. The official plans indicate "butt connections" throughout and we have no reason to think otherwise. The point, however, is that either system could have been employed on any particular ship.

We can easily quote good authority on the use, or misuse of technical language, even by experienced seamen, which is, however, readily accepted by equally experienced shipbuilders and constructors who are interested in facts rather than creating doubts through semantic manipulation.

In "HMS *Victory*, Building, Restoration and Repair", by Arthur Bugler, O.B.E., Late Constructor at HM Dockyard, Portsmouth, published in 1966, we note the reference to the "Remark Book" of Mr. R. F. Roberts, a midshipman in the *Victory* during the Battle off Cadiz, 21 December 1805.

Mr. Roberts describes the Battle Damage sustained by *Victory*. The author (Bugler) does not hesitate to comment that "Roberts was a seaman," and in reference to some of the nomenclature, "Roberts was not however a shipbuilder and he may not have used quite the right terms when dealing with the hull."

The above should clearly illustrate that which we have endeavoured to prove throughout these pages. No one doubts the intent of Mr. Roberts when, through his ignorance of technical terms relating to hull structure, he misused the nomenclature.

On the other hand, his familiarity with masts and rigging produced a good description of damage to the top hamper.

Many of Mr. Chapelle's interpretations should be considered carefuly: "Unaccountable nautical and shipbuilding phrases. . . ." It is unreasonable to expect every research analyst, transcriber, archivist, and typist to be a professional naval architect.

He says that "no record of a model exists." Again, he supposes that as we have not *seen* it (after 174 years), it did not and does not exist! There is an old story of an Indian Scout reporting to Daniel Boone that "there are no injuns ahead".—Replied Boone, "Wouldn't it be closer to the truth if you reported that you saw no Indians ahead"! More on the "model" later (p. 143)!

Let us examine another example of Mr. Chapelle's interpretations, regarding the Capps Report: under "Masts and Rigging," 'sail yard' is listed as part of the spars attached to the bowsprit. "No such spar name can be found. . . ." he tells us, in the dictionaries. Even the youngest tyro, after rigging his first model would appreciate this "word game" and fill in the missing "sprit" as one of the spars affixed to a bowsprit, completing the word *"spritsail" yard*.

Page 51

All too often, Mr. Chapelle refers to the several bloopers committed in the *Capps Report* as "Polland, p. _____." We hope it is not his intent to shift the error from that report to this writer. "Next (Polland, p. 35) it is stated that the *Constellation* was 'Hauled in the Washington Navy Yard in January 1812. . . .'" This writer, of course, made no such statement, but was merely quoting the Capps Report.

Mr. Chapelle, we hope, knows very well that an inexperienced person standing on the berth deck, may often refer to the lodge and dagger knees within his view as belonging to that (berth) deck when in fact these elements would be supporting the gun deck above and should rightfully be referred to a *gun deck knees*. At this writing, we do not know who actually edited the Capps Report but we are thankful that, at least, the information was recorded, even if it must be cautiously interpreted.

Still on the Capps Report, Mr. Chapelle sees, "on the 'Spar-Deck' something called a 'bowsprit hook'" and cannot possibly imagine what in the world this could be! This writer has noted such nomenclature in several pieces of old correspondence, even a reference to the *"sprit hook."* Assuming that Mr. Chapelle's dictionaries include "breast hook," may we take the opportunity to suggest he put two and two together. He will find the answer to be a breast hook supporting the bowsprit in the bed of that spar.

Next, Mr. Chapelle is puzzled by "new 'fore and mainsail sheet bitts' (Polland, p. 37)." "It is to be feared" he says that "the 'transcriber' or author went adrift," and we agree, but he did the best he could! Is it inconceivable that the "transcriber" or author (as he says) meant *fore and main topsail sheet bitts?* Such errors are typical of transcribers and typists. They are seldom committed as is an author who generally has a good idea of his subject matter.

Next we quote—"all new plank to 'anchor ports,' whatever these were . . . ." Well, these were and are *bridle ports* just forward of the number 1 gun ports used in fishing the anchor. In that crowded area of the gun deck, most of the space is occupied by the manger and either a chain stopper, a hawser bill, or both as is the case here. In addition, of course, we have the hawser itself, to say nothing of the large messenger. This makes it almost impossible to place a cannon at the ports on each side of the eyes of the ship. These openings, however, are ideally situated to work the fish tackle for the anchor.

The subject of purely professional language from those we would most expect to hear it from can become almost comical in the extreme. Our attention has lately been directed to an article in the *Bath Independent*, 6 September 1884. Captain Manson of the *Percy V* steaming past the big *Henry B. Hyde* asked, "How much should you suppose those five fastenings on the rudder of that ship weigh?" Now, it would be reasonable to assume that each and all of those "professionals" described by Mr. Chapelle and by this writer, as a matter of fact, would expect Captain Manson to have more appropriately asked "How much . . . the *rudder pintles and gudgeons* weighed."

Again, we must wonder at Mr. Chapelle's statement concerning the several inappropriate terms used: "This is the way it stands in Polland's paper at any rate: a collection of errors in nautical nomenclature." This writer must again state that every honest effort was made to quote *verbatum, the Capps Report* including the obvious errors. This is already indicated in the 1966 S.N.A.M.E. paper. The errors are in the report and *not* in my writing. We note: Mr. Chapelle's, "It is needless to discuss most of Mr. Polland's statements in his summary. . . ." Needless? It has been a curious fact in this "debate" that Mr. Chapelle's publication now under discussion is contained in 51 pages, almost all of which are devoted to his rather colorful comments on the aforementioned 1961 article of *16 pages*. As for his continued "kind" comments on the 1966 S.N.A.M.E. paper, he devotes himself almost entirely to the Capps Report; *ten pages out of 131*. This is almost incredible considering the "scholarly" label attached to this work.

Page 54

Mr. Chapelle places much weight on the spelling of the name of the Chief of the Bureau of Construction and Repair,—"Harte" or "Hartt"—and we have seen it spelled both ways several times. Next we note—"The paper Polland, 1966, pp. 113–131 contains a 'Glossary of Terms . . .' but unfortunately does not contain any of the terminology in question. . . ." Now, why would I incorporate such incorrect verbiage into my own glossary? I do not believe it to be overemphasizing my own "professional status" to state that I, too, may recognize an error in terminology.

In any case, select sections in Part 3 are presented as they appear in the S.N.A.M.E. paper. It is suggested that the reader note the extent of missing comments that might have appeared in Mr. Chapelle's manuscript, had he reported on the full scope of that paper.

NOTES

[1] CHARLES SCARLETT, JR., and others, "Yankee Race Horse: The U.S.S. *Constellation*," Maryland Historical Magazine (March 1961), vol. 56, no. 1, pp. 15–31.

[2] LEON D. POLLAND, *The Frigate "Constellation": An Outline of the Present Restoration*, 1st and 2d ed. (Society of Naval Architects and Marine Engineers, 1966 and 1968).

[3] SCARLETT and others, loc. cit.

[4] LOUIS GOTTSCHALK, *Understanding History* (New York: Alfred A. Knopf, Inc., 1961). Page 139: "What is meant by calling a particular credible is not that it is actually what happened but it is as close to what actually happened as we can learn from a critical examination of the best available sources." Page 199: "One rule is certain: if a historical datum is relevant, it may not be discarded. . . ."

[5] SCARLETT, loc. cit. (footnote 1).

[6] *Naval Documents Relating to the Barbary Wars* (Washington, D.C.: United States Government Printing Office, 1939), vol. 1, p. 69. Authorization Act of 27 April 1794.

[7] Ibid.

[8] Ibid., Letter from Secretary of War to Secretary of the Treasury 21 April 1794 referring to Progress report by the Secretary of the Navy to the House of Representatives.

[9] Ibid., p. 124. Progress Report of 12 December 1795.

[10] Ibid., p. 150. Act of Congress of 20 April 1796 giving authorization to sell materials not needed.

[11] *Naval Documents Relating to the Quasi-War with France, February 1797–October 1798* (Washington, D.C.: United States Government Printing Office, 1935), [vol. 1], p. 211.

[12] Ibid., August 1799–December 1799, [vol. 4], p. 472. Quoting *The Norfolk Herald,* 3 December 1799.

[13] Ibid., April 1799–July 1799, [vol. 3], p. 377. Quoting the *Federal Gazette and Baltimore Daily Advertiser* of 20 June 1799.

[14] Ibid., August 1799–December 1799, [vol. 4], p. 327.

[15] Ibid., p. 328.

[16] POLLAND, op. cit., (footnote 2), 1st ed., p. 006.

[17] Record Group 19: Records of the Bureau Ships (National Archives, Washington, D.C.). Letter from Captain Samuel Breese, Commanding Officer, Navy Yard, Gosport, to Joseph Smith, Chief, Bureau of Yards and Docks, 24 February 1853. See also Record Group 181: Records of the Naval District and Shore Establishment, Bureau of Yards and Docks Correspondence for January–June 1853; letter of 28 January indicates *Constellation* hauled up on 23 February.

[18] *Quasi-War with France, February 1797–October 1798* (footnote 11), [vol. 1], pp. 298–299. Letter from Truxtun to Cowper 15 August 1798.

[19] Ibid., pp. 298–302.

[20] Ibid., pp. 302–303. Letter from Truxtun to Cowper 16 August 1798.

[21] Ibid., January 1800–May 1800, [vol. 5], p. 419.

[22] Transcription from the original in the Josiah Fox Papers, MS, Peabody Marine Museum, Salem, Massachusetts). Retranscription in Files of *Constellation* Restoration Committee.

[23] Record Group 45: Naval Records Collection of the Office of Naval Records and Library, Entry 374: The War Department Records of the Federal Government, 1790–1831. (National Archives, Washington, D.C.) Letters sent concerning Naval matters, October 1790–June 1798.

[24] GOTTSCHALK, op. cit. (footnote 4).

[25] *Constellation* file (Library of Naval War College, U.S. Naval Training Station, Newport, Rhode Island). Transcribed letter.

[26] Record Group 71: Records of Bureau of Yards and Docks, Navy Yard, Gosport Log Book 1851–1855 (National Archives, Washington, D.C.). Letters from Commandant, Gosport Navy Yard January–June 1853; November 1853–May 1854.

[27] *Constellation* file. Transcribed letter from David Stodder to Thomas Truxtun, 14 April 1795.

[28] *Constellation* file (footnote 25).

[29] National Archives Record Group 45, Entry 374 (footnote 23).

[30] Pickering file (Historical Society of Pennsylvania, Philadelphia, Pennsylvania).

[31] National Archives Record Group 19 (footnote 17). Plan of Transverse Sections, C&R Plan 107–13–4B dated February 1853.

[32] National Archives Record Group 45 (footnote 23). Transcribed sheet from the Delano notebook, circa 1853.

[33] CHARLES DESMOND, *Wooden Shipbuilding* (New York: Rudder Publishing Co., 1919), pp. 27–58.

[34] National Archives Record Group 19 (footnote 17). Letter from Samuel Breese, Commanding Officer, Gosport Navy Yard, to Commander Joseph Smith, Chief, Bureau of Yards and Docks, Washington, 3 June 1853.

[35] Pickering file (footnote 30).

[36] National Archives Record Group 19 (footnote 17). C&R Plan 107–13–4A.

[37] National Archives Record Group 45 (footnote 23). Also GOTTSCHAULK, op. cit. (footnote 22), p. 139.

[38] National Archives Record Group 45 (footnote 23), Subject Files: file ZB. Letter from 'near Wheeling, Va." to the Honorable Samuel Southard, Secretary of the Navy, 27 November 1826.

[39] National Archives Record Group 45, Entry 374 (footnote 23).

[40] Ibid., Letter from War Office to Joshua Humphreys, 6 September 1796.

[41] Ibid., Letter from War Office to Tench Francis, Esquire, 29 June 1795.

[42] National Archives Record Group 45, Entry 374 (footnote 23).

[43] Ibid.

[44] *Constellation* file (footnote 25).

[45] National Archives Record Group 71 (footnote 26).

[46] HOWARD I. CHAPELLE, *The History of the American Sailing Navy* (New York: W. W. Norton and Company, Inc., 1949), p. 468.

[47] POLLAND, op. cit. (footnote 2), p. 17.

[48] Ibid., p. 100.

[49] Ibid. Quoted letter from Truxtun to Secretary of the Navy, 16 August 1798, Truxtun's Letter Book 1798–1799 (MS 12, Historical Society of Pennsylvania, Philadelphia, Pennsylvania).

[50] POLLAND, op. cit. (footnote 2).

[51] National Archives Record Group 45 (footnote 23). Plan (fragment) of *Constellation,* Mizzen Mast Survey 1840 (1829).

PART 3

An Outline of the Present Restoration

Introduction

IN THE TRANSACTIONS of this Society dated New York, 10–11 December 1914, there appears a paper entitled "Our First Frigates" [1]. This work contributed by the then Acting Secretary of the Navy, Franklin Delano Roosevelt, was well received and in discussion the late Rear Admiral Washington L. Capps commented that, "no paper presented . . . has greater human interest than the one prepared at such pains by the Assistant Secretary of the Navy. He has embodied in this comparatively brief paper much data that intimately relate to work now being done by members of this Society." [2]

Further record of the interest shown by our late President in the early American Navy and in particular his interest in the *Constellation* is contained in his Papers dated May 1919, entitled "Early Construction of Frigates and U.S.S. Constellation (Yankee Racehorse)". [3]

This is not meant to imply that the Restoration Committee blindly followed the writings of Roosevelt. It was noted that his manuscripts were, in many cases, undocumented. During 1960–61, the Committee undertook the task of authenticating his work, exhibiting documentary references and in some cases supporting evidence in the nature of archeological finds in the hull of the ship. Since that time, several of the documents involved have proven invalid or otherwise unsupported by primary evidence and have since been discarded.

Franklin D. Roosevelt's interest was natural enough, inherited from Theodore Roosevelt, a recognized naval historian. [4] T. Roosevelt's collection of naval historical documents was apparently lost when the Newport Naval Training Station Repository was destroyed by fire in January 1946. This apparently included many of the remaining manuscripts and plans relating to *Constellation*.

Fire took a heavy toll of *Constellation's* historical references when the Norfolk Navy Yard was burned in 1861 by Union Forces and earlier when the Washington Yard was destroyed in 1812 by Captain Thomas Tingey to keep it out of the hands of the advancing British forces.

The first consideration of the Construction and Repair Committee, herein referred to as "CRC," was to restore the ship to as early a period as possible without destruction

---

From a paper presented before the Chesapeake and Hampton Roads Sections of the Society of Naval Architects and Marine Engineers at Baltimore, 1966 and revised 1968.

of major additions and alterations which *materially illustrate the orderly progression of naval architecture*. The second criteria for preservation in lieu of restoration of detail was almost wholly dependent upon soundness of structure.

Over the years, since the inception of the Construction and Repair Unit of the *Constellation* Committee, hundreds of construction notes have been recorded and assembled. These notes form the principle background for this paper.

From the construction notes and related documents, new plans were executed taking into account references dating back to the earliest conception of *Constellation's* dimensions as published in the "American State Papers" [5] and to the shipyard of David Stodder on Harris Creek in Baltimore when the ship began to rise out of the stocks in 1795.

An appraisal of a rather large body of evidence, slowly but inexorably accumulating will be shown to support the historical and physical integrity of this ship as the *Constellation* of Captain Thomas Truxtun, 1797. She has known many changes but her identity remains unimpaired.

A special commission was activated by the U.S. Department of the Interior to investigate the findings of the Committee in order to make the most intelligent evaluation of *Constellation's* historical and structural integrity. Those findings are totally recorded herein. As a result of the review of the U.S. Department of the Interior, *Constellation* was presented with a bronze plaque designating her a National Historic Shrine.

General Discussion

I N JUNE OF 1959 the initial survey was begun. As the ship was approached from shoreside, it was immediately noted that she bore but a vague resemblance to a frigate of the period 1797–1812. A closer study of the hull appeared to indicate that if this was indeed the ship launched in Harris Creek, Baltimore, over a century and a half before, several tremendous changes had occurred in her profile. More specifically, five primary distinctions separated this hull from the recognizable profile of Commodore Thomas Truxtun's Frigate of 1797.

1. The square transom of the early ship was here represented by a round or elliptical shape.
2. The tumblehome of the hull appeared to be much reduced in comparison to the early frigates.
3. The decorative head rails, so distinctive on the early ships, were nowhere to be seen, being totally enclosed in an evelope of deteriorating timber. The outline of the head could not conceal the straight line rails of a later period as opposed to the delicately "bagged" rails of the early ships.
4. The hull was said to have been lengthened by 12 feet.
5. The spar deck bulwarks now consisted only of an outsized hammock rail. The masts and spars were now on the beach rapidly deteriorating almost precluding any thoughts of total preservation. As quickly as possible these elements of the top hamper were coated with preservative and further protected until work could begin.

At this time, the new planking on the port side had already been installed from the water to the level of the lower gun port sills (about the 12-foot to the 25-foot water-line). It was obvious, however, that the main wale strakes had been omitted. A mental note was made to correct this deficiency at a later date.

When the initial survey was complete, it was decided to replank the starboard side installing 6 x 9 inch and 6 x 10 inch wales, 6 planks in width, of fir timber, the upper-most strake in way of the gun deck beams at the 24-foot waterline. The wales moulding 2 inches thicker than the adjacent strakes provide additional longitudinal strength along the length of the transversely framed hull.

Little had been accomplished at this time in recording the condition of the oak framing timbers on the port side now newly planked to the vicinity of the 25-foot waterline.

CRC immediately drew up a plan of these frames that were in way of the small area still open, which afforded a view of the upper futtocks. This plan while sadly incomplete, illustrates in the open area the new additions, the earlier timbers, and what appeared to be parts of even earlier structure. Thus was established a precedent and cultivation of a work habit which was to remain with the committee during the long months and years to come. Every detail was to be recorded even though at the time it may have appeared to be an insignificant event.

The starboard side of the hull, now ready for restoration, was, of course, an entirely different matter. The condition and extent of repairs to each frame was noted and later recorded on a print prepared for that purpose. More than 100 photographs were made involving each frame from stem to stern.

As noted before, *Constellation* in 1959 bore little, if any, resemblance to a frigate of 1797, but it should be carefully pointed out that the element of disguise is forever present—if this was indeed the ship launched on 7 September 1797. In the course of several reconstructions her appearance could have changed considerably. It was a matter of some concern to the Baltimore committee that some definite indication of the ship's historical integrity be established and this was to be no mean task, although CRC had one distinct advantage. The background of research when summed up would not alone be limited to library information and technical data from archives but here within reach was the ship herself awaiting minute examination of every timber, bolt, and trunnel.

Simultaneously with the inception of the Construction and Repair Committee, then known as the Technical Advisory Committee, every available plan or sketch of the ship was integrated into a central file. These principally consisted of several spar and gun deck plans, a Lines Plan, circa 1888 [6] which was traced from a plan by John Lenthall dated May 1853,[7] a Sail Plan of 1904 and a Docking Plan of 1946.[8] Last but far from least, a poor copy of a plan by William Doughty in 1794 draughted under direction of Joshua Humphrey [9] of Philadelphia. The original of this plan is located at the U.S. Naval Academy, Annapolis; however, it took little more than a glance to note that the contours of this old drawing did not coincide with the later plans of 1853. Closer examination of the plans substantiated CRC's first impressions that the ship, in her present form at least and from what could be seen of her topsides, did not represent an early American frigate. In addition to the reduced tumblehome amidships, the bows appeared to have been thinned out considerably and forming a graceful flair from the 2-foot waterline to the rail. If this be the product of a designer of 1797, then he was indeed a man or rare, farsighted instinct for it was several decades before the fore bodies generally reached this stage of development.

It was now noted by the plans that the *frame spacing differed by six inches!*

An honest evaluation of material and observation thus far assimilated could only lead to certain conclusions. The ship fitted out as a sloop-of-war and riding so peacefully at her berth in Baltimore almost certainly appeared to be represented by John Lenthall's plan of 1853,[10] drawn a half century following the launching of Frigate "E," the alphabetical designation of the ship christened *Constellation*.

This apparent setback to the integrity of the ship was closely followed by the realization that several vessels had been "administratively rebuilt" by the Navy in the decades preceding the Civil War. Funds for new naval shipbuilding were nonexistent being almost entirely cut off by an apathetic Congress.

That austere body, however, neglected to consider the resourcefulness of the Navy and approved funds for repairs, reconstructions, and conversions. Later evidence testifies that several old ships-of-war had entered various Navy Yards in a program designed to modernize the fleet but in the process had mysteriously disappeared, broken up completely and an entirely new ship substituted, bearing the original name. Thus was an old ship "Administratively Rebuilt" and it was now becoming alarmingly evident that the old *Constellation* "may have" disappeared in the same manner when she was brought out of "ordinary" in January 1853. A search of the records in 1963 showed, however, that in no case had the Navy denied the fact that in several cases new ships had replaced the originals.

It was in this rather heavy atmosphere that the Committee surveyed its position. Under existing circumstances reconstruction could continue on the lines of a sloop-of-war originally built in 1853–1855. Work would largely center around replacement of deteriorated timbers, plank for plank and beam for beam, until the present ship, once more built anew, would reflect the profile of the Civil War Navy.

Active research would be minimized; documentary and physical characteristics of the ship already providing the basis for the restoration.

Somehow it all seemed too simple. CRC at this moment could not pretend to have followed through on its original intent to conduct an intensive research program. In any event where does the historian end his research? Is there ever really an end?

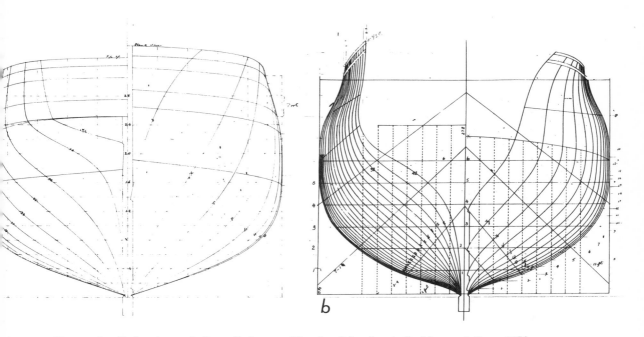

FIGURE 1.—Body plans of *Constellation:* a, Plan by John Lenthall, May and June 1853; b, Humphreys/Doughty, 1795.

Looking back, actually little had been accomplished other than the interpretation of two plans drawn a half century apart. There could be but one obvious conclusion and it was acted upon almost immediately. A search for documentary material was initiated through the Baltimore Public Libraries, the Peabody Library, and the Maryland Historical Society; these being the local and most obvious repositories. Simultaneously, correspondence and personal contact was opened with the National Archives in Washington. Before the second anniversary of this program, over 50 separate assaults had been made on the files at the National Archives alone.

As the search broadened, the Committee's activities included the Pennsylvania Historical Society, the Franklin Institute in Philadelphia, the Franklin D. Roosevelt Library in Hyde Park, New York, the Naval War College Library, Newport, Rhode Island, the Boston Navy Yard, the Washington Navy Yard and many others.

Meanwhile, much remained to be done at the shipsite. Through the months of July and August 1959, various measurements were taken along the decks and athwart the beams. Deck heights were recorded as well as framing and beam dimensions including the length on waterline and beam moulded to outside of frames and shell planking.

The result of these recordings appeared to justify the physical characteristics to the plan of John Lenthall laid down in May 1853. It was noted, however, that the gun deck was sheathed with 3½-inch white pine planking making a total thickness of 7½ inches, the original planking below being 4 x 7 inch oak and pine. In July of 1964 the sheathing was finally stripped off baring the deck once more. These dimensions were carefully recorded, it being already established that the height of gun port sills from the deck at the sides bore a definite relationship to the type and caliber of cannon. This dimension may well furnish another clue to the history of *Constellation*.

Although the spar deck above is alluded to as the weather deck, the upper 'tween deck, known as the gun deck, is by no means tight in the modern concept. The 14-inch high hatch coamings are designed to deflect water and debris from entering the decks below. The gun deck itself may be considered to be technically open to the elements due mainly to the nonwatertight gun ports, hatches, scuppers, and hawse holes. With the main pumps in operation, a flood of water is discharged over this deck from the well, in the after section of the main hold.

Further description of the gun deck arrangement would include the riding bitts set up with sampson knees and notched in way of beams no. 7 and 9, in the gun deck and through to the berth deck. The aft pair of bitts were cut off flush at the deck plank many years ago and at this moment new oak timbers are shaped and scarphed into place. The forward bitts were well worn and had been trimmed from 17 inch square to cylindrical shapes; their pedestals are today still square cut. The plans of 1888 [11] indicate both pairs of bitts, rounded and still in use. The new aft set of hawser bitts are built of oak 17 inches square, as were the original forward bitts, complete with cross bar.

Between the fore and after bitts, the camboose was located and described as we soon discovered by Commodore Thomas Truxtun in his letter book.[12] Dagger knees under the spar deck, fore and aft, are considered to be in generally good repair, only three requiring restoration.

Shelf knees in the deckhead were in various stages of decay, the weather having penetrated the spar deck plank permitting concentrations of water to be trapped above the knees and beams.

The upper clamps as well as spirketing and waterway timber were found to be generally affected by wet-rot. These elements were completely renewed in the summer of 1964.

Dagger and hanging knees in way of the main hatch are of wrought iron, 31-inch arm, 42-inch leg and 3¾ inches wide and were probably installed in 1853–55 although such supporting structure was proposed for ships before 1800.[13] The French *Insurgent,* captured by *Constellation* in 1799 was found to have iron knees.

The mooring arrangement at the gun deck level includes a "stopper bill" on the port side and a hawser clamp starboard providing means to employ a semimodern chain hawser to port and a hemp hawser to starboard.

The capstan is located on centerline at frame 18, ratcheted in the deck and directly connected to an additional drum on the quarter deck. Thus, manpower may be applied by 60 or more people if necessary on both levels to raise the (8100 pound) anchors or to hoist the heavy spars.

The double bilge pumps located at frames 11 and 12 centerline are of early vintage, however, in use well past the Civil War period. They are identical to those found on *Constitution*.

Another set of single lift pumps are indicated by obvious cuts in the deck at frame 8; however, they too are long removed and are not shown on the new plans.

Before the end of 1959 the research files included a direct and clear reproduction of Lenthall's plan of May 1853 which contained the lines, half breadths and inboard profile.[14] Here, then, was the basic plan about which in the following notes all others would depend. To supplement this plan, the offsets and dimensions of 1853 were located in the National Archives. Thereafter, dimensions taken from the work could be directly correlated with the source of origin, it no longer being necessary to scale off the drawings, a rather hazardous procedure.

As the survey gained momentum, the obvious discrepancy, that of length between perpendiculars assumed heightened significance. The official offsets clearly indicated 176 feet B.P. (between perpendiculars) as did Lenthall's lines plan, and finally confirmed by physical dimensions taken from the work.

If in the event that *Constellation* actually was lengthened by 12 feet from what was universally known to be 164 feet B.P., would it be unreasonable to suspect that somewhere in this hull such evidence existed in the form of fastenings, timber cuts, or other pecularities in the structure?

In the spring of 1960 a portion of Lenthall's plan was discovered in the library of Franklin D. Roosevelt. This was the inboard profile from the foremast aft to amidships. A curious vertical line drawn through frame F, initialed *F.D.R.* was labeled *"New 12' Aft of line."* [15]

At this writing, the sources of the late President's material are not all known to us, indeed his papers contain few footnotes. The truth was often manifest in archeological evidence. In the present case, it was obvious that a concentrated survey be carried out in way of frame F.

Inspection of the lower futtocks and floors at this level was necessarily deferred, the frames being hidden behind the ceiling timbers and completely covered by pig iron ballast bars in the hold below (Figures 14 and 13, Part 3).

It is not here implied that conclusive evidence has come to light merely on the basis of a notation on a drawing even though it be immediately followed by the "discovery" of a repair in the ship. It is a sad fact that conclusions have been published based entirely on library research. As this report develops, futtock timbers E, F, G, H, and I will be further discussed.

FIGURE 2.—Fragment of an Inboard Profile from the forehold aft to amidships by John Lenthall (Franklin D. Roosevelt Library, Hyde Park, New York).

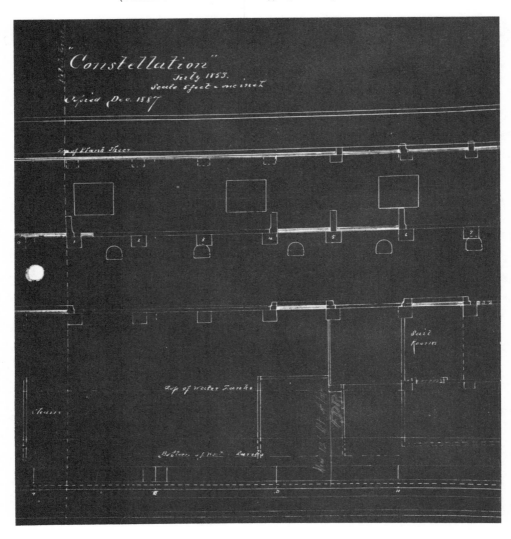

Back at the drawing board, where Lenthall's plan lay open, it was next observed that the four upper breast hooks are "hatched in" on the drawing while the lower three in the fore hold were not thus shaded. Whatever the meaning, these details were again carefully surveyed on the ship. It was noted that the three lower hooks appeared to be of a much earlier vintage and they clearly indicated the difference in condition, coloring, and texture of wood. The difference is to be noted by comparing the later hatch beams and girders on the upper decks, with those on the orlop and berth decks, amidships. In most cases, the lower structure shows a strikingly darker complexion. The later breast hooks as found in the upper sections are hatched in on the new plans and match those of Lenthall's drawing. Deadwood and all keel pieces are also included in the new plan of the Inboard Works (Figure 3).

The exposed orlop breast hook although badly strained, remains intact and still satisfactorily contributes to the strength of the bow assembly.

On 24 June 1959 the first new construction plan was begun. This was to become the Inboard Profile and Deck Plan, including Spar and Gun Decks [16] (Figure 3).

It was planned to construct the new drawings to criteria laid down by the lines of 1853 and 1888 with the further objective of altering the work in accordance with latest research material. Although tracing and scaling from the old prints proved to be a tedious task, it was well worth the effort. Before it was even completed, the plan provided a basis for comparative analysis of several generations of ship construction superimposed, momentarily, on this same plan.

At the Franklin Institute in Philadelphia the journal of Thomas Truxtun was located.[17] This was to prove invaluable as the Captain went to great lengths to set down a detailed description of each deck level.

The deck plans of 1888 [18] show among later innovations, curved fife rails in way of the fore and main masts on the old fighting ships carried these fixtures squared off on two sides. They were generally quite large in order to accommodate as much of the running gear as possible. This cleared the spar deck bulwarks for the fighting crew and boarding parties.

It was recognized quite early in the restoration that CRC should become familiar with the original design of *Constellation,* as well as with her contemporaries in the original fleet of six ships authorized by Congress on 27 March 1974 [19]: *United States Constitution, President, Congress, Constellation, Chesapeake.* It soon become habitual to study available plans of these ships in order to firmly establish the design and peculiarities of a typical frigate of 1797–1800.

Of no less importance were the later designs of the 1850s and the ships preceding them. The *Constellation* that sailed out of the Gosport Navy Yard in 1855 bore a marked resemblance to the new corvettes, from the water to the rail at least. There was little comparison, however, in the underwater body. Boilers, coal bunkers, and driving gear took their toll of available space below in the new steamers, resulting in considerable filling out of the underwater lines. Block coefficients expanded from about .45 to about .65 or .70. The decrease in deadrise is evident when comparing the body plan of the *Hartford* built in Boston in 1858, with Humphrey's *Congress* and *Constellation* plan for example, or again with the lines of our ship as she cleared Gosport in 1855.

In the months following the discovery of the 1853 offsets, many plans and related documents found their way into the ship's growing files. Included among these are the following statements:

From the notes of Captain Tingey of the Washington Navy Yard in December 1811: "this ship has a strange feature, in that she is very sharp forward, and this probably accounts for her great speed. . . ." [20]

Truxtun to Livingston, 22 May 1798: "I must say though we probably have a better ship through the efforts of Major David Stodder—the constructor here . . . his new ideas in the form of the bow will most likely increase the speed through the water of the hull. . . . I praised Stodder's ideas and his launch was most successful. . . ." [21]

The notebook of Constructor Delano of Gosport in 1853 in which we find: "Underwater body of Constellation does not match drawing of Humphrey's Plan, or the sketched drawings 1852. . . ." [22]

Although the above are typewritten transcriptions they are included for the record on the basis of their very existence.

Letter of Captain Charles H. Bell of sloop *Constellation* to Secretary of the Navy, 3 November 1855, on his first cruise: "I have found the sailing quality of the Constellation much to my liking, *since the extension of the body.* I do however find that the head spacing should have been raised in the 'tween decks and that *many of her* old knees should have been replaced in the last conversion. . . ." [23] (italics mine).

As late as November 1926 at the Philadelphia Navy Yard [24] the docking master tried to use the Humphrey plan "to construct the keel blocks and hull bracing." It was found, almost too late, that "her form did not match the prints."

These statements were to be of inestimable importance in the evaluation of *Constellation*'s integrity; however, none was as significant as the letter from David Stodder, the builder of *Constellation* dated 30 April 1795 to the Secretary of War, Timothy Pickering in which he states "Timber and room [frame spacing] [is] 32 in. . . ." [25] This statement seemed quite definitely to identify the "Old" *Constellation* and the ship now in Baltimore, *as the same!* The letter itself, proved to be one of the most significant finds of our research. He also states here that the keel is 18 inches broad while the 1853 offsets indicate a 17-inch keel.

This letter (Figure 4) also contains several original characteristics of the ship as constructed: "The bolting the floor of the ship is one of the most essential parts, tho' the weight of a bolt of $1\frac{7}{8}$ of an Inch is as much as two of $1\frac{3}{8}$ of an Inch, yet I am convinced *that* Bolt cannot possibly answer the same purpose as the *two* therefore it must be wrong.—The Keel is 18 In broad Timber & room 32 In. . . ."

It would be quite impossible to alter the spacing of the frames without completely destroying the identity of a ship. Such could not be the case here as this dimension, 32 inches is now shown to be constant from 1795 to the present time. On the plan of "Sections" (1853) there is a note also and a small insert sketch indicating the "Old" frame spacing as 32 inches (Figure 6, Part 2). [26] Considering that "Constructor" Delano apparently found that these sections did not fit the ship, [27] it was decided by CRC to make additional overlays traced from these sections. When placed over the plan of Joshua Humphreys, it was apparent that these lines were mistakenly

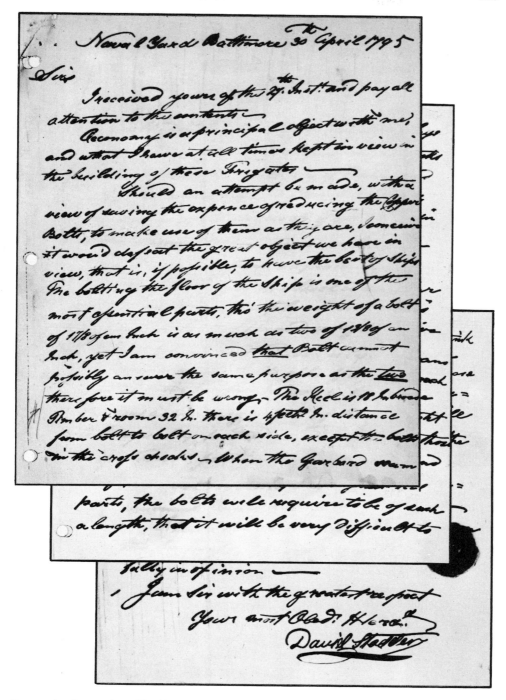

FIGURE 4.—Letter from David Stodder to Timothy Pickering, 30 April 1795 (Pickering File, Historical Society of Pennsylvania, Philadelphia, Pennsylvania).

taken from that plan. It was evident that each section in Delano's drawing of 1853 matched precisely the corresponding station in Humphreys' plan. Another indication that Humphreys' plan was not the basis for the finished lines of this ship.

At first it appeared that these sections were taken off the ship while docked, the offsets being shown outboard of the hull. The Gosport Log for 17 January 1853, however, tells us only that "*Constellation* was docked for the purpose of getting her bilgeways under her for hauling her up." [28]

By way of further explanation, it should be noted that the ship was at the least "razeed" down to the berth deck in the vicinity of the 22-foot waterline and in many areas cut down to the floor timbers. In 1853, however, sound frames were apparently left standing. Thus it was that the ship came down through the ensuing years, to her berth, back in the Port of Baltimore in 1955. Of course, this proof existed entirely on paper, at that point, but by the spring of 1960, work had already begun to remove the outboard planking from the starboard side. It was then anticipated that the structure of the framing timbers would reveal something to prove or disclaim the integrity of the ship.

On 6 December 1796, Stodder and Truxtun received permission from the War Office to delete the diagonal riders from the hull structure.[29]

At the time of the committee's first survey of *Constitution* in Boston, CRC made it a point to check the diagonal riders of that ship only to find that during her reconstruction in 1856, or perhaps later, these large timbers were never replaced.

Undoubtedly Stodder fully concurred with Truxtun on the deletion of the diagonal riders. His own experience was by this time well known and more than a little respected in the capital.[30] Quite often he found himself at odds with Truxtun on technicalities of design but they must have both been aware that the British ships of lighter scantlings did not carry diagonal riders.

This hull stiffening may have been very well on Humphreys' merchant ship designs, especially those engaged in the bulk trades where heavy loads were imposed upon the lower hull structure.

The unequal distribution of buoyancy along the length of a ship is inherent in a normally efficient hull design, due to rapid changes in sectional shapes at the extremities. This is largely responsible for the condition known as "hogging" or drooping at the ends. A large percentage of the logitudinal strengths of a wooden hull lies in the outside planking and the ceilings; however, a glaring deficiency lies in the total absence of edge fastenings, as employed in modern welding and riveting methods.

By the very characteristics of the wood and the included fastenings (iron and copper bolts, tree nails, etc.) it is not possible to realize the full strength of the structure. Invariably an unwelcome flexibility is induced in the hull, as the fastenings "work" in the timbers, resulting in a permanent hog as the weight of the hull at the extremities slowly overcomes the buoyancy. The distribution of loads, therefore, in a wooden ship should be carefully planned, even though the ship is lying in still water. It was this condition that the diagonal riders were designed to offset, It is doubtful, however, that the additional time, which would have been considerable, and expense in building would have justified them. There was trouble enough it seems in the procurement of timber from the coast of Georgia.[31]

After about two years on the stocks, there was little to show in the way of progress, although the other frigates were certainly no further along the way. To John Morgan had fallen the task of locating and getting out the live oak for the framing timbers. He was sent to the mouth of the Savannah River and upon delivery, he was to become the constructor at Norfolk for the frigate to be built there.[32] Live oak, with several times the durability of the white oak employed in French and British ships, could conservatively be estimated to remain serviceable for 25 years, perhaps even a half century. Cutting the timber to the moulds, dragging it out, and loading it aboard ships for the perilous coastal voyage to the building yard was another matter.

Morgan's correspondence records the terrible conditions under which he labored with the few men he could hold. Continuous downpours of rain kept the men and the work virtually underwater, and disease added to the troubles. Ships were wrecked on the way to Baltimore and the delivery was many months behind schedule.[33]

All evidence pointed to the assumption that during the "great reconstruction" of 1853–55, the tumblehome had been altered and the length increased. Now with the outside planking and the inner ceiling in process of removal, CRC found the opportunity to check-out the documentary evidence and theories with an archeological study of the now exposed frames. As each strake was removed upwards from the 15-foot waterline and progressing to the plank sheer, the newly exposed timbers were photographed for future reference and each futtock section of each frame was inspected for identifying tool marks, number of bolts, frequency of bolt holes, bolt material (iron or copper), elongation of bolt holes, and apparent condition, texture, and age of frames, in direct comparison with adjacent timber, length of futtocks, and shifting of butts.

As the inspection got underway, particular attention was concentrated on the area, supposed, by Franklin D. Roosevelt, to have been added between frames B, C, D, and E and the after sister of frame F in 1853. It was found instead that frames E, F, G, and H and the after sister of frame I showed evidence of being later additions. Thus, Mr. Roosevelt's notation overlapped CRC's findings. These four frames contained at least 60 percent fewer bolt holes than their counterparts which, it appeared had been subjected to several resheathings before the existence of frames E, F, G, and H. Another most revealing characteristic of these four frames, extending up to the plank sheer, was that they were obviously cut and shaped in a *saw mill*. The rotary blade markings were quite clear on the frame sidings. In striking contrast, all adjacent remaining frames showed evidence of having been hand hewn on all four sides.

The lengthening of a ship's hull should not be considered an innovation of the mid-19th century. This practice extended back many years in the shipyards and is of course, common even today. Both Theodore Roosevelt in his *Naval War of 1812*[34] and James Fenimore Cooper in his *Naval History of the United States*[35] show the frigate *Adams* cut down to a sloop and lengthened at the Washington Navy Yard in 1812. This was but one of several which were "administratively rebuilt."

Returning to *Constellation,* the latest and strangest discovery was that several of the earlier frames extended from the plank sheer down to the turn of the bilge and out of sight, in one continuous long arm. The survey team had expected to find all the frames assembled from at· least four futtocks and this was generally the case with several exceptions as noted here. These exceptions are indicated on a plan made for the purpose of recording these findings.[36]

When the outer planking was finally and completely stripped down to the 15-foot waterline in 1960, there was exposed to view in many areas, several generations of timber. Chocks, facing timbers, and patches were discriminately sewn into room and space and worked into the frames in the top timbers. This condition prevailed from the gun deck to the plank sheer. Allowing for later repairs, such as that of 1888 and including work performed in 1904, still remained those most important *hand hewn timbers* which at this point were considered to pre-date the 1853 reconstruction. It appeared that the "moment of truth" was close at hand. When did the tumblehome (or the original moulded sectional shape) actually begin the transition?

The crews had not been satisfied with the excessive rolling characteristics (which can be counteracted by a reduction in tumblehome) from the first, until 1812, when *Constellation* entered the Washington Navy Yard under the supervision of Captain Tingey. If we can believe the Newsport, Rhode Island Naval Training Station transcripts, both Captains Truxtun and Murray had tried to remedy the excessive tumblehome by relocating the bulwarks.[37] Truxtun claimed, however, that *Constellation* was one of the fastest ships afloat in spite of this uncomfortable roll. She was often referred to as "The Yankee Race Horse" following the victory over the French *La Vengeance* in February 1800. This claim is not surprising, however, as many captains as well as the crews often referred to their own ships as the fastest afloat.

There is evidence that the lower shrouds were continually rubbing on the bulwark rails causing excessive strains and obvious stretching and chaffing damage. Captain Tingey stated that he could improve the situation by adjusting the tumblehome to the angle of shrouds and at the same time strengthening the hull.[38]

Evidence up to this point leads one to believe that when *Constellation* left Washington in January 1813, her wale planking had been increased on each side by 7 inches over the side planking, her sectional shape in way of the upper timbers was somewhat altered and she was materially a "better ship than when she left the stocks in Baltimore," to quote Captain Tingey and later, Franklin D. Roosevelt in his historical outline of *Constellation, Constitution,* and *United States.*[39]

Thus, it would seem Captain Tingey increased the water plane area, a function of stability. He increased the transverse metacentric height at the same time, adjusting the tumblehome which in turn increased the righting moment of the ship and stabilizing the uncomfortable roll.

Another item to be taken into account is the long length frames extending from the vicinity of the spar deck beams to below the turn of the bilge. These are undoubtedly early timbers (pre-1853), judging by the excessive number of bolt holes and obvious marks of the adz.

There is on file in the ship's archives at least one sheet of the semi-monthly progress report, dated 15 July 1839, indicating the extent of work.[40]

Of special interest is the notation that the "air ports were caulked" during this repair. Also listed as finished and to be finished in 1829 are the following items: Ship's head, quarter galleries, capstan, rudder to be hung, iron work on the hull, spar deck bulwarks caulked, gun ports, lifting pump, fore pump, plumbing, lower masts, top masts, yards and cross trees, sprit sail yard, half main yard, tanks, cooperage, gun carriages, carronade carriages, boats, sails repaired and replaced, all rigging reworked, bower, sheet and kedge anchors and hawsers repaired, 213 new top timbers and futtocks, 68 new third futtocks, 53 second futtocks, 27 first futtocks and 9 new strakes under the wales. It was from documents such as this that the Capps Report must surely have originated.

This should provide some indication of the extent of work done at that time; however, much more was accomplished, including rework on the aft orlop deck.

It was becoming obvious, viewing the naked frames, that the razee line in 1853 occurred at or about the 22-foot waterline and when the sheath was removed, as CRC was redoing, the futtock timbers above and below that line were renewed, then as now, "*as necessary.*" Considering the long length frames which reach above and below that line, it seems apparent that the tumblehome was not altered in 1853. The spacing of gun ports was altered to accommodate the new heavy guns and this necessitated in many cases the shortening of upper futtocks in way of the lower port sills.

Before closing the discussion on the long length frames, it may be well to consider that this may be one of the principal points relative to the extreme longevity of *Constellation*.

It is a matter of record that well before restoration was started on *Constitution* in 1923, it was found that many of her frames were in *short lengths*. On her reconstruction plans, CRC counted as many as five futtocks making up her framing structure. The butts were found to have shifted in the frames and she was badly distorted; 11½ inches wider on her port side than on the starboard. Her stem was 8¾ inches to port; and a 14½ inch hog was found in the hull.[41]

Constellation on the other hand, while greatly weakened structually through the years of neglect never experienced this near disaster. She was at sea under her own sail long after *Constitution* was honorably retired.

It is also noted that the increased frame spacing or "Timber and Room," (over that of, for example, *Constitution*) does not necessarily bear the connotation that more dead space exists between the frames, thus making for a lighter construction. On the contrary, the total siding of sistered frames being 24 inches substracted from the spacing of 32 inches, leaves a remaining dead space of but 8 inches.

In comparison, the siding of sistered frames on *Constitution* is 13 inches and the space between frames is an additional *13 inches* totaling the 26 inch room and space of Humphrey's design.

The spacing is measured from the fore side of the forward sister of one frame, to the corresponding or fore side of an adjacent frame. Thus we see that the mass of framing timber presented on *Constellation,* contributes materially to the strength of the hull. The molded dimensions of the frames are practically equal on both ships. This should provide some indication of the strength of *Constellation*'s hull structure in direct relation to one which, a great ship in her own right, aptly earned the title of "Old Ironsides."

The tumblehome then was apparently altered by Tingey in the Washington Navy Yard when the sides were increased in 1812–13 [42] and again to conform to modernization in 1839. There is little doubt that she was razeed in 1853.

During the restoration in 1960, it was decided to raise the spar deck bulwarks to approximate their original positions on the new inboard profile.

CRC now had in its growing files a photostatic copy of a elevation plan of the stern, dated 1840 and used for a survey of the mizzen mast.[43] This clearly indicates the raised spar deck bulwarks *around the perimeter of the rounded stern 11 years before the rebuilding of 1853*. Even then, this was not an original thought.[44]

Further examination of this plan revealed in the vicinity of the waterline a minutely inscribed date—"1829" (See Figure 20, Part 2.) This indicated that the mizzen mast survey was carried out in 1840 on the old plan thus saving the expense of a new drawing, a perfectly acceptable procedure. Armed with this information, the committee could safely conclude that the rounded stern concept of the frigate with full taffrail bulwarks did indeed trace back 24 years before work began in 1853. This, incidentally pointed directly to Samuel Humphreys' statement in 1829 on the same subject. The plan also indicates the arrangement of the stern decorations and a good view of the quarter galleries just as they appear now. These are shown on the outboard profile of 1960, precisely as they were at that period.

An interesting sidelight on the rounded stern appears on an engraving by J. Yeager in a treatise on shipbuilding published in the Edinborough Encyclopedia, 1819. This fine drawing depicts various gun bearings as determined on the square sterned British frigate *Boadicea* compared with the round sterned *Hamadryad*. Apart from our earlier conclusions that the sailing characteristics are materially improved by eliminating the square transom, it became clear that considerable energy was expended in experiments covering the arrangements of the artillery thus defending the adoption

FIGURE 5.—Stern profiles of *Constellation:* a, 1829–1840; b, present.

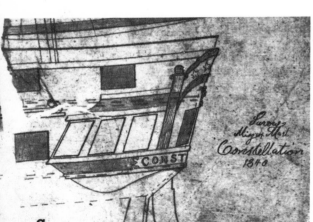

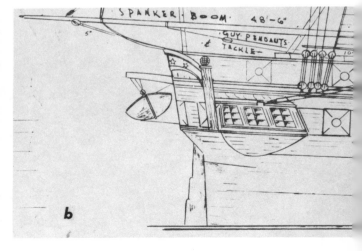

of the curvilineal stern. There is an obvious advantage in the more concentrated distribution of fire power with guns trained through the after broadside ports, quarter and stern ports of the round sterned *Hamadryad* frigate.

Thoroughout the final stages of the conception of the reconstruction plans, a ghost had appeared to haunt the seemingly well conceived analysis of the presentation of deck arrangements.

In Capps Report under "Major Repairing, 1829," there appears a statement referring to a notation of the Construction and Repair Department, 1828. This statement is in reference to a *forecastle and a quarterdeck*.[45]

It was somewhat of a shock for CRC to suddenly learn of an apparently nebulous structure, the design of which was something of a mystery at that moment.

It was thus decided to continue along the lines of the Committee's original plan, to restore the spar deck as indicated by the presently existing structure, and where necessary to fall back upon the growing file of contemporaries, in order to arrive at what was known to be "typical." It was reasoned, therefore, that subsequent alterations could be incorporated when significant documentary evidence presented itself.

The hatch was covered with portable gratings or wooden hatch covers permitting the ship's boats to be stowed thereon, or lowered to the gun deck below, by means of a gallows at the aft part and a belfrey at the fore part.

A diamond netting was rigged in the gangway between the fore and aft bulwarks, in way of the hatch and secured to stanchions. This seemed to parallel the known description of the 32-gun Essex designed by William Hackett.[46]

It was decided to further investigate the weather deck arrangements of several other ships, perhaps a step earlier in the eighteenth century.

Returning to the model collection at the Naval Academy attention was drawn to an English ship model No. 43 in the collection.[47] Here, the huge main hatch extended from side to side and from the quarter deck to a focs'l deck. This fit the description perfectly, including runways, or gangways, on each side.

Thus, it may be determined that the alleged focs'l and quarter decks on *Constellation* were actually the extremities of the spar deck level, being in effect the spar deck itself, a forecastle and quarter deck, if some prefer that nomenclature, divided by the unusually large main hatch area which, with the portable gratings and tarpaulin cover in place,[48] presented a flush deck appearance.

If this theory is acceptable, *Constellation* would bear a marked resemblance to *Essex* in the upper works and the weather deck. A check of the lines plan, however, reveals no such similarity below the bulwarks, which is not surprising. That ship, hurriedly though expertly designed by a man of advanced maturity, reflected a somewhat earlier period in her beautiful contours.

It should be noted that the description as suggested above, draws the original design of *Constellation* even further afield from that of Joshua Humphreys whose designs indicate no such arrangement.[49]

It is probable that the raised poop deck and focs'l "effect" was illusioned by the fact that the main hatch may have originally extended almost from the fore mast to the main mast and from side to side of the waist. This is quite possible as such an arrangement is described in a letter by Charles Stewart, filed in the Library of Congress.[50] This

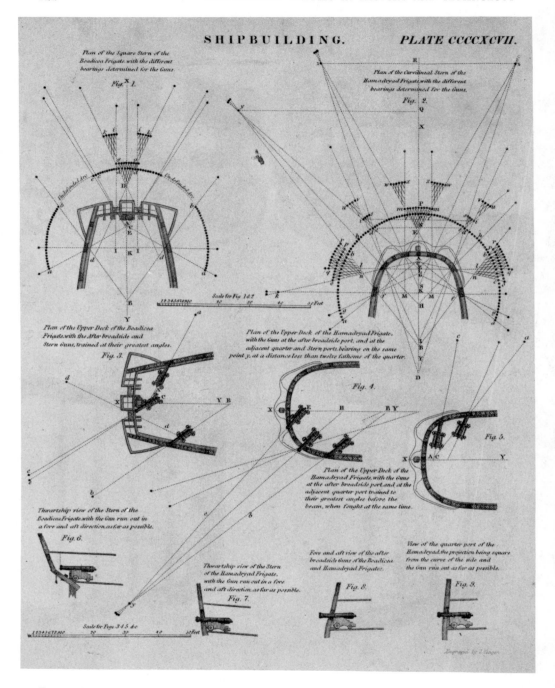

FIGURE 6.—Gun bearings on the rounded stern of H.M.S. *Hamadryad* and the square sterned *Boadicea*. (From Encyclopedia Britannica, 1819.) Note the advantage of the gun bearings on *Hamadryad*.

FIGURE 7.—*Constellation* during present reconstruction at Pier 4,
Baltimore, Maryland, August 1968.

letter unfortunately is a transcribed copy and CRC hesitated to alter the plans and structure without the blessing of an original document. At this writing, the committee is still seeking out the original of this letter.

Accompanying an article by Captain Raymond J. Toner in the October 1956 issue of Naval Institute Proceedings is a fine drawing of *Essex* under sail. It is noted that the gangway nettings and figures of the crew apparently abreast of the gangway in way of the hatch certainly advance the open waist theory. The hammock rails also are fitted on the after bulwarks so as not to impair vision over the forward rails.

Attention was again focused on Thomas Truxtun's description of the spar (or upper) deck.[51] His account, running from aft to forward, describes the arrangement of the sky lights, steering wheel, masts, bitts, capstan, etc., and the "long gratings" (undoubtedly the hatch area) between fore and main masts but also with chocks for spare spars along the gratings. This is certainly the earliest and most original description of *Constellation* known to us.

Evidence certainly points to the fact that the main hatch area on the spar deck originally extended from side to side of the waist, and literally from the foremast to the main mast. This was apparently true at least until the repairs of 1829.[52] The main hatch as depicted on the restoration plans of 1959 [53] is the result of relocating the side girders flush with the ladder wells at each end. This increased the width of the hatch from 7 feet 10 inches to 15 feet 0 inches, thus typifying a frigate hatch, 12 inches wider than that now on *Constitution*. The length of the hatch was increased (by including the ladder wells) from 30 feet 6 inches to 42 feet, between stations 11 and 19.[54]

Figure 8 shows the spar deck, as it was found and reconstructed to show the huge main hatch as it may have appeared sometime in the earlier period as suggested above. The opening extends from side to side with fore and aft gangways. The inside dimensions, as altered are 26 feet 4 inches wide $\times$ 42 feet long, between stations 11 and 19 (see also Figure 3).

In order to arrive at this location and the included dimensions of the opening, the forward hatch end beam was relocated as far as possible in the direction of the fore mast. This extended the opening to the vicinity of the galley smoke pipe scuttle at station 9. Deducting the 12-foot extension of the hull in 1853, the fore end of the hatch would be back at station 11, which is directly in way of the lengthened section of 1853.

This then, it was assumed, is as far forward as the end beam could locate. Moreover it was the present location of the extreme end of the ladder well! This would certainly simplify the reconstruction. The after hatch end beam was found to be located as near the main mast as possible, precluding any problems there in the longitudinal dimension.

Worthy of special note are the "long gratings," between the fore and mainmasts, in the journal of Thomas Truxtun,[55] copy of which is on file in the ship's archives. Allowing for a gangway 2 feet 10 inches wide on each side of the open area the resulting sketch is presumed to show the "huge main hatch" as it may have appeared in the earlier days of the ship. If the main hatch were now to be extended notwithstanding the addition in length, the resultant clear opening would be approximately 54 feet long as indicated by Figure 8B. This is assumed to be far out of proportion in contemporary design.

Of course, a certain amount of conjecture, as well as intuition, and what is defensively known as "feel" for the subject must be called upon to visualize the probable hatch plan in its earliest form. The inherent weakness of this "feel," however, is that it is often employed to hedge around the truth or to afford cover when research has been neglected.

Figure 8 is included to show the extent of the hatch opening as at first planned and to afford a measure of comparison. It is typical and quite similar to that now found on *Constitution*. Figure 8A depicts the hatch as finally reconstructed.

From contemporary plans and descriptions, the runways were dropped 9 inches below the deck providing a step-down in way of the hatch between the fore and quarter decks. This feature is in compliance with ships of the period.

It has been repeatedly conjectured that *Constellation* was different from all others but how "different" can she get? There is always to be considered the traditional architecture of every historic period and the painfully slow changes which are finally brought about. For this reason, sudden and radical architectural changes in the restoration are brought about only after a long hard look at convincing evidence. The

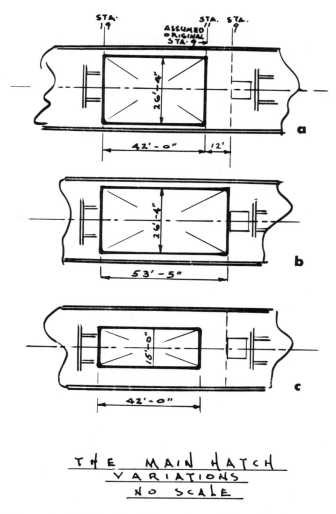

FIGURE 8.—Main hatch variations of spar deck: a, Final reconstruction, b, previously considered dimensions; c, dimensions as found in 1955.

"drop" of 9 inches represents the difference between the moulded dimension of the deck beams (9 x 13 inches) and their removal, setting the runways on lighter beams 3 x 8 inch dimensions at the lower extremities of the existing timbers. It is noted that the hatchway on the gun deck, also partly in way of this area, appears to be an addition of 1853–55. It is located in way of stations 11 to 13, or frames H to D, or within the 12-foot body extension beams. This is not surprising, as the gun deck is certainly a product of the 1853–55 rebuilding. This hatch provided greater additional access for ship's stores and relieved the congestion or traffic for the large crew.

A surprising discovery was that of a hawse pipe located on the berth deck between stations 15 and 16 on the port side. Directly over this pipe in the deckhead, the space between the beams had been chocked with heavy solid timbers with the apparent intention of increasing the scantlings in way of the now missing structural support of the hawse pipe foundations on the gun deck. A patch on the berth deck, starboard side is evidence of the removal of the hawser pipe on that level. This is somewhat confusing as no straight line run is provided from the gun deck to the hold. The evidence, of course, would indicate the presence of a chain locker below between frames 1 and 4 or approximately 10 feet forward of the present locker.

At the National Archives a drawing came to light signed, S. T. Harte, dated 11 July 1855. This is a plan of capacities illustrating the stowage and arrangements of the berth deck and the hold. It shows the various items of consumable stores, kentledge, fuel ammunition, etc.[56] By direct comparison this plan lists the dimensions of the "old" and the "new" *Constellation,* illustrating the increase in capacity of the rebuilt ship, thus tying the "new" and the "old" together as the same ship. What would be the purpose of this comparison of two entirely different ships on a single plan? If one ship was deliberately destroyed, would not such a comparison be irrelevant? That plan is sadly deteriorated and could not be reproduced here.

The same method of comparison in present day lengthening or "jumboizing" of a hull may be employed; the "old" designation being used as reference to the ship before jumboizing into its new status as a larger ship. At this writing, scores of World War II tankers and cargo ships have been so lengthened.

It is of interest to note the original dimensions given on the above plan as 164 feet by 40 feet 6 inch moulded beam. Probably an error, but in any case another additional bit of confusion.

Lenthall in his recommendations to the Secretary of the Navy dated 18 December 1851 sets the moulded beam at 41 feet 0 inch.[57] This was well before work began on 26 February 1853 so we were at least on firm ground again.

The term "moulded (or molded) beam" has been a continual source of unreconcilable dimensions from the very beginning of the present restoration. CRC had long been aware that the moulded beam, relating to wooden ships is generally measured to the *outside of plank.* It was, therefore, surprising to find this dimension in Lenthall's correspondence as well as on the offsets of 1853 taken outside the *frame.* Further, some have indicated this dimension at the *extreme breadth* of the ship,[58] while others appear to have referred to the geometrical midpoint at the midship section. In view of the foregoing, it would not be surprising to find the moulded beam referenced at the pitch line which is 10 feet abaft the extreme breadth. Coincidentally, the half breadth at the pitch line is 3 inches shorter than that dimension at the extreme beam, or 40 feet 6 inches as indicated on the National Archives plan, dated 11 July 1855.

It is noted on the body plan of 1853 that the baseline is calculated as the lower rabbet of the keel and the first vertical dimension is measured to the upper rabbet. It is from this point that the moulded edges of the main frames originate. Scaling athwart Lenthall's plan at the 18-foot waterline and at the extreme longitudinal breadth the result is 41 feet.

In summary, following John Lenthall's practice of measuring the moulded beam, it is evident that this dimension was 41 feet 0 inches prior to the Gosport reconstruction;

it was 41 feet 0 inches when the work was completed; and it is 41 feet 0 inches today. In order to reconcile this dimension, the measurement was duplicated on the ship with identical results. In order to coordinate the present work with the 1853 drawings as well as the offsets of this year, the new construction plans of 1959–68 reflect the moulded beam at outer edge of the frames.

Another plan also came to CRC's attention. This was a profile plan of the ship, No. 128584, also in the National Archives dated November 1855, just 4 months later than the one in the Boston Navy Yard.[59] This was apparently the result of an inspection of the outside hull planking. It pinpoints the plank fastenings (copper bolts, iron bolts, and tree nails) from stem to stern. *In way of the lengthened section* the number of bolt markings drop to insignificance. This strikes the eye immediately, upon glancing over the plan. It is brought to the attention of the reader, only to show another instance of repeated differentiation in the many documents noted involved the "mysterious" 12 feet of additional length. This work, it should be remembered, is set down because it is felt important that the findings of the committee be recorded along with an evaluation of these documents.

We would like now to introduce two notations from the log of the Gosport Navy Yard, 1851–1855. The first dated 20 November 1854, well after the reconstructed ship was launched, refers to the *Frigate Constellation,* moved from the new wharf. The second entree dated 21 July 1855 again refers to the *Frigate Constellation.*[60]

In the closing statements of Admiral Capps' report, he makes the significant observation that "the new Constellation was actually built from the basic structure of the old frigate *Constellation* and must be classified as a new ship." [61]

These words it is believed sum up the key points of difference in any debate on the originality of this ship. She *"was* actually built from the basic structure of the old frigate . . ." (italics mine). This is a definite statement without reservation and must be accepted as such without further manipulation of language. The second half of the statement, "and must be classified as a new ship," must be taken as a straight-forward opinion of that author.

The opportunity has been seized upon before to make such quotes only as it suits the individual. For example, if we were to here quote but half of the above quotation while omitting the other, as has been done before, we could easily slant a view in either direction; i.e., a half truth. In the same closing paragraph Capps notes that the English and French Navies, the world's greatest fleets at the time, both classified such ships as "the same older model, even though their molds and shapes do *not match* the original vessel" (italics mine).[62]

Throughout the months of July and August 1959, measurements were taken along the decks and athwart the beams at various strategic points. The results of these tests proved that the plans of 1853 were in agreement with the physical characteristics of the ship. This necessarily meant scaling off the plans; however, the search team soon turned up the official "Dimensions and Offsets" dated 1853 at the National Archives. Before CRC was to complete this initial phase of research, there would be over 50 trips to the National Archives *alone.* It was here that the committee now concentrated its efforts to determine what pertinent information might be in the files.

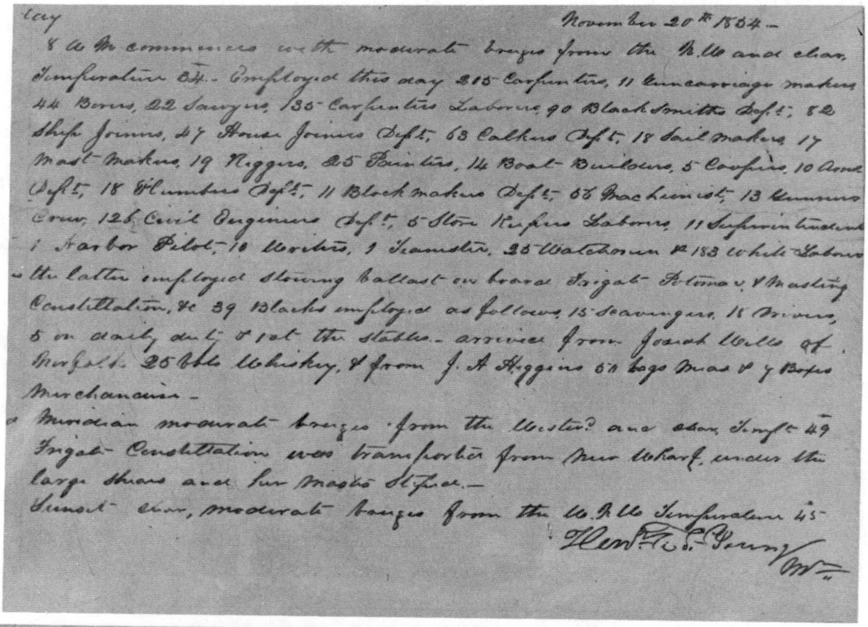

day November 20th 1854 -

8 A M commences with moderate breezes from the N.W and clear. Temperature 34 - Employed this day 215 Carpenters, 11 Gun carriage makers 44 Borers, 22 Sawyers, 135 Carpenters Laborers, 90 Black Smiths Dept; 82 Ship Joiners, 47 House Joiners Dept, 63 Calkers Dept, 18 Sail makers, 17 Mast makers, 19 Riggers, 25 Painters, 14 Boat Builders, 5 Coopers, 10 Armd Dept, 18 Plumbers Dept, 11 Blockmakers Dept, 66 Machinist, 13 Gunners Crew, 126 Civil Engineers Dept, 5 Store Keepers Laborers, 11 Superintendents 1 Harbor Pilot, 10 Writers, 1 Teamster, 25 Watchmen & 133 White Laborers - the latter employed stowing ballast on board Frigate Potomac & Masting Constellation, &c 39 Blacks employed as follows 15 Scavengers, 16 Drivers, 5 on daily duty & 1 at the stables - arrived from Josiah Wells of Norfolk 25 bbls Whiskey, & from J. A. Higgins 50 bags Mas & 7 Boxes Merchandise -

Meridian moderate breezes from the Westward and clear. Temp 49 Frigate Constellation was transported from New Wharf, under the large shears and her masts stepped. -

Sunset clear, moderate breezes from the W.N.W Temperature 45

Henry A. Young
Mr

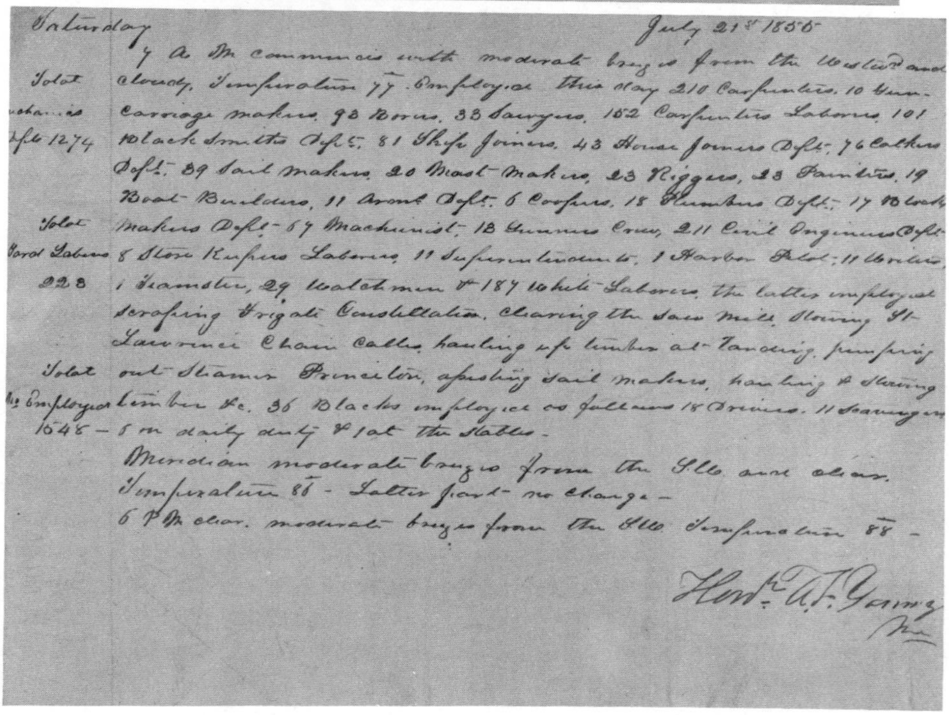

Saturday July 21st 1855

7 A M commences with moderate breezes from the Westward and cloudy, Temperature 77. Employed this day 210 Carpenters, 10 Gun-carriage makers, 93 Borers, 33 Sawyers, 152 Carpenters Laborers, 101 Black Smiths Dept, 81 Ship Joiners, 43 House Joiners Dept, 76 Calkers Dept, 39 Sail makers, 20 Mast makers, 23 Riggers, 23 Painters, 19 Boat Builders, 11 Armd Dept, 6 Coopers, 18 Plumbers Dept, 17 Block makers Dept, 67 Machinist, 13 Gunners Crew, 211 Civil Engineers Dept, 8 Store Keepers Laborers, 11 Superintendents, 1 Harbor Pilot, 11 Writers, 1 Teamster, 29 Watchmen & 187 White Laborers, the latter employed scraping Frigate Constellation, clearing the saw mill, stowing St. Lawrence Chain Cables, hauling up timber at Landing, pumping out Steamer Princeton, assisting sail makers, hauling & stowing timber &c. 36 Blacks employed as follows 18 Drivers, 11 Scavengers 5 on daily duty & 1 at the stables -

Total mechanics Dept 1274

Total Yard Laborers 228

Total Nos Employed 1548

Meridian moderate breezes from the SW and clear. Temperature 86 - Latter part no change -

6 P M clear, moderate breezes from the SW Temperature 88 -

Henry A. Young
Mr

FIGURE 9.—Notations from Gosport Log Book referring to the "Frigate" *Constellation,* after alteration to the hull, dated 20 November 1854 and 21 July 1855.

Meanwhile, the first plan (Figure 3) was on the drawing board, 24 June 1959. This was to be the Inboard Works and Deck Plans (Spar and Gun Decks).[83] Basic dimensions for this plan were taken from the work existing on the ship and checked against the plans of 1888 and the lines of 1853–55. Frames and deck beams were measured on the ship for moulding and siding as well as spacing and breadth of beam moulded. Also checked against these plans were the deck heights, dimensions of hatchways, carlings and half beams, as well as length between perpendiculars and length on each deck. Deck planking thicknesses and beam dimensions were determined as well as shell planking, dimensions of individual frames, keelsons, floors, limber strakes, mast steps, deadwood, steam and apron, knightheads, bowsprit bitts, etc.

In the course of surveying the area, just forward of the waist in the main hold, it was discovered that the bitter end of the old bower chain was still secured to the keelson, at frame D. While the iron parts give promise of an early vintage, it appeared at the time that the keelson itself was built into the ship later, in 1853–55. This probability was derived from several sources, including the Gosport Stores Report covering these years. This report was to prove of inestimable value as research progressed.[64]

In order to provide proper identification and location of details, throughout the ship, each deck beam was numbered from the bow and progressing aft to station 33 near the transom. This information was indicated above the inboard profile on the plan while the frame or station numbers were put in their proper place, below the keel. All deck beam dimensions were taken from the actual work and spacing measured from fore side to fore side of beams. With the offsets of 1853 at hand,[65] it was possible to begin work on a preliminary plan of lines and half breadths, as well as a body plan.[66]

There are several immediate necessities for this plan. For one thing, the spar deck bulwarks no longer existed in their original form. If the ship was to be authentically restored, the bulwarks must be reconstructed, faithfully following the existing curve of tumblehome. In order to accomplish this, the draftsman must search his mind as well as his conscience in attempting to project himself and his drawing board back, well over a century to a remote corner of the Gosport Navy Yard, in hopes perhaps of catching the thoughts of Constructor Delano and John Lenthall. What would happen if it was assumed that the bulwark timberheads were merely sheared off in way of the spar deck even though the razee line may be lower? [67]

It was resolved to take the offsets of 1853 [68] and along with a new preliminary body plan, create a fair curve and new offsets extending upwards to a height of 4 feet 10 inches above the top of the spar deck beams.

It is well known that typical early plans of Joshua Humphreys show an open rail running practically the length of the spar deck.[69] It appears highly improbable, however, that any of the American ships of this first fleet went to sea without bulwarks of one kind or another protecting the weather deck batteries. Several trial sketches were drawn with gunwales completely encircling the perimeter of the deck. The 1853 offsets [70] extended up only to the corvette plank sheer at the spar deck but it was now necessary to reach a point in space topping the proposed old style bulwarks.

After several sketches were drawn, it was decided to raise the bulwarks from frame H forward to frame V and from frame 9 aft, around the curved stern. The profile thus developed on the lines plan projected backwards in time through Lenthall, Delano and Tingey to the area of Stodder and Truxtun.[71]

It was found that by continuing the existing curve of the body plan up to a point 4 feet 10 inches above the top of the spar deck beams at the side, a tumblehome of 3 feet ⅛ inch was created by gently reversing the curve above the sheer strake. Selecting five planks, 4 x 9 inches wide for the sheath and ceiling this brought the height to 3 feet 9 inches and capping with a 4 x 12-inch plank sheer and a 9-inch waterway over the deck beam the gun'ls reached the desired 4 feet 10 inches height allowing for caulking between planks. A new set of points were thus developed from these lines and added to the half breadths and waterline heights in the offsets of 1853.[72]

From the offsets, a completely new drawing (Figure 10) was laid out at one-quarter inch scale, which reverted back to the creation of the lines of John Lenthall, including what at the time appeared to be the addition of 12 feet to the length between perpendiculars in way of frames F and I. In addition the plan featured the newly projected spar deck "frigate" bulwarks.

The hawse pieces and knightheads contribute to the formation of a breakwater. This structure is shown on the plan, but with the additional eye appealing "fashioning pieces" sweeping down to the level of the kevel rail at frame "a". Four timberheads are shown on this plan, as they are also shown on the Spar Deck plan and on the Inboard Profile.[73] As pointed out, they are located at Stations X, Y, Z, and "a," and are stiff legged between the frames, in this case to secure the greatest strength through the resulting faying surfaces, and bolted together.[74] The catheads are relocated forward between stations Z and "a" in order to meet the upward sweep of the newly curved seat rails (not shown on the lines plan) which must stand away from the bridle port. For additional strength the "knee" type catheads were replaced with the "beam" type, an earlier arrangement. This also eliminates a potentially susceptible area of wet rot such as was found on the sheer strake and adjacent planking under the knee.

At frame V, the rail is shown raised to a height of 4 feet 10 inches above the top of spar deck beams. This height is held back to frame H, in way of the forward main hatch beam at station 11. Here, the line at top of plank sheer drops on the plan to the same level as shown by John Lenthall, 13 inches above top of spar deck beams. This provides ample space for loading in way of the main hatch (42 feet 0 inches long clear opening) sweeping back to frame 9. Here the plank sheer rises again to the height of 4 feet 10 inches. Topping the plank sheer at the quarters are the hammock rail cranes. The gangway in the bulwark is secured by a diamond netting when the ship is at sea.

The intersection of the forward perpendicular is shown at the 17-foot waterline and the forward edge of the rabbet of the stem. Similarly the aft perpendicular intercepts the aft edge of the rabbet of the stern post at the 17-foot waterline.

The Lenthall plan indicates the fore edge of the keel 12 feet 9 inches aft of the forward perpendicular, and the forefoot of the stem is hook scarphed for a distance of 5 feet 6 inches, over the top side of the keel. The cutwater at the forefoot was shown hooking under the keel and fairing into the fore edge of the false keel. These details did not agree with the actual structure as noted when *Constellation* was drydocked (see drydocking, p. 141).

Waterlines are shown for the cutwater, independent, and bobstay pieces, as well as for the trailboards progressing to the top of the billet head 37 feet 8½ inches above the baseline, or lower rabbet of the keel. In the body plan, the hawse pieces and cavils are shown as are the relocated and reconstructed spar deck bulwarks.

In the half breadths of the lines plan, waterlines are shown from the 2 foot 0 inch waterline to the top of plank sheer. Here, also, the new spar deck bulwarks are depicted in proper perspective. Camber of decks, or spring of the beam of 5 inches, is shown in the sheer lines.

It is noted that in the body plan and in the half breadths it was thought unnecessary to add the usual diagonal fairing lines and projections for the purpose of checking out the fairings along the length of the hull at various heights and stations. These lines were later added and when projected on the plan show the pleasing and efficient fore and aft contours (Figure 10). What were John Lenthall's thoughts in 1853 when he arrived at the same point of reconstruction? By the laws of geometry, when a theorem has been proven, that theorem may henceforth be used as fact without question in further constructions. At this writing, it is obviously needless to prove a fact that has been in existence for over a century and a half. It was equally needless for Lenthall to prove the same fact.[75]

Then what indeed *were* John Lenthall's thoughts in 1853? The author feels a certain kinship to this man who certainly was not one to be frivolous with the use of that element of time. He needed no fairing lines on his body plan of *Constellation,* and they are equally superfluous today for practical purposes. This committee has gone through literally hundreds of pieces of his voluminous correspondence; much of which is located at the Naval Academy at Annapolis. In a letter to Skinner,[76] Lenthall gives the original dimensions of the ship and the cost of repairs in 1829, 1832, 1835, and in 1840. He also says, that the length may be easily increased, even to *240 feet,* though at the expense of longitudinal strength. This was in answer to a proposal by Silas Stringham to increase the beam to 55 feet and the length to 240 feet. This was a ridiculous proposal by a man who 10 years later, however, was to command a well-organized naval attack on Hatteras, but whose knowledge of naval architecture and ship construction was apparently limited.

Another letter by Captain Skinner dated the very next day, December 19th to Navy Secretary Graham also politely rejects Stringham's proposal (Figure 11).

The offsets and dimensions were taken bodily from those of 1853 and carefully typed on linen strips, 9½ x 30 inches long. To these were added the new dimensions expanded from the new sheer, half breadths, and body plans, at their proper locations in the risings of sheer and the half breadths of square frames, fore and aft. The strips were then taped together, forming the new plan of dimensions and offsets (plan No. C–100–5) [77] and a permanent reproducible print was made directly from this, as were all the new plans, to insure against loss or destruction of the originals. On 1 November 1964 CRC received from the Boston Navy Yard several plans and tracings representing the work of 1946. Among these tracings is a reproduction of Joshua Humphreys' lines plan, all too obviously drawn in preparation for docking *Constellation!* Here was remarkable proof of the sad waste of time and effort to say nothing of the potential danger imposed upon the ship. This indicates the most recent repetition of the

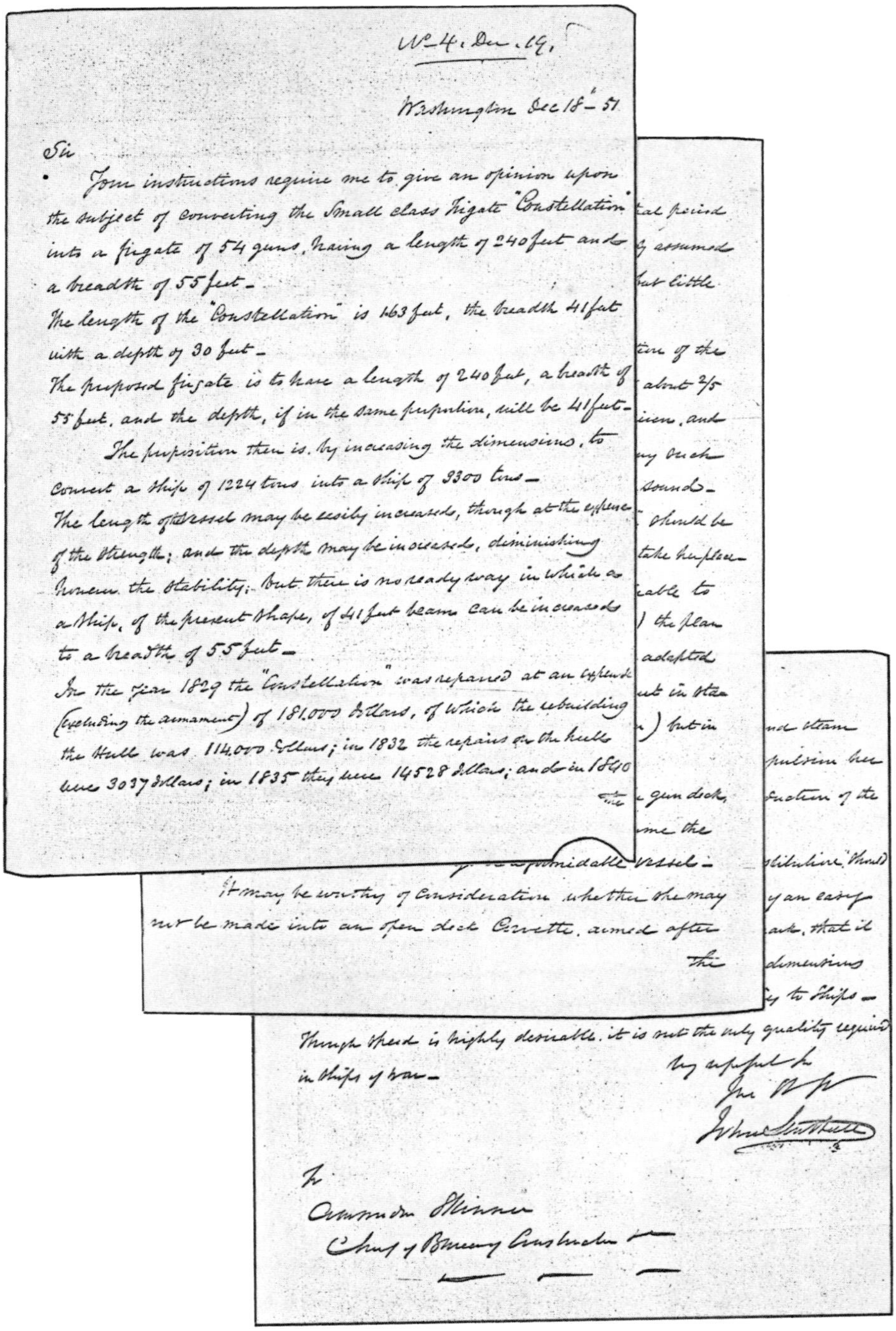

No 4. Dec. 19.

Washington Dec 18th 51

Sir

Your instructions require me to give an opinion upon the subject of converting the Small class Frigate "Constellation" into a frigate of 54 guns, having a length of 240 feet and a breadth of 55 feet —

The length of the "Constellation" is 163 feet, the breadth 41 feet with a depth of 30 feet —

The proposed frigate is to have a length of 240 feet, a breadth of 55 feet, and the depth, if in the same proportion, will be 41 feet —

The proposition then is, by increasing the dimensions, to convert a ship of 1224 tons into a ship of 3300 tons —

The length of the vessel may be easily increased, though at the expense of the strength; and the depth may be increased, diminishing however the stability; but there is no ready way in which a ship, of the present shape, of 41 feet beam can be increased to a breadth of 55 feet —

In the year 1829 the "Constellation" was repaired at an expense (excluding the armament) of 181,000 dollars, of which the rebuilding the Hull was 114,000 dollars; in 1832 the repairs on the hulls were 3037 dollars; in 1835 they were 14528 dollars; and in 1840

... a formidable vessel —

It may be worthy of consideration whether she may not be made into an open deck Corvette, armed after ...

Though speed is highly desirable, it is not the only quality required in ships of war —

Very respectfully
Your Obt Servt
John Lenthall

To
Commodore Skinner
Chief of Bureau Construction —

FIGURE 11.—Letter from John Lenthall to Commodore Skinner, 18 December 1851. (National Archives, Washington, D.C., Record Group 45).

same error. Down through 152 years everyone it seems, reached for what appeared to be the original building plan. A bit of research into previous dockings in each case could have saved a great deal of effort.

Unbelievably, to carry this theme further, there was received by CRC a Docking Plan dated 30 September *1946,* made at the Boston Navy Yard.[78] The basis for this drawing is obviously an early and incorrect draught, the Humphreys' plan of 1794. All dimensions, however, including the 18 inch broad keel were apparently taken from that plan. This is also the 18-inch keel siding mentioned by Stodder (Figure 4). The Boston plan is closely followed and superseded by a corrected plan dated 22 October, 3 weeks later.[79] The profile, however, still remains incorrect. It shows the wrong stem and cutwater and the bowsprit entree is through the spar deck, instead of bearing on the hook at the gun deck. At first glance, one might assume it to be perfectly natural that the ship's contours did not agree with that plan in 1946 nor did it agree in 1926 in Philadelphia.[80] It is simple enough to reason that a new ship was built in 1853, but what about 1852 and 1812 if we are to believe the transcribed correspondence in our files? Delano and Tingey in those years also appear to have found that the ship and Humphreys' plan were incompatible.

The beakhead structure in 1959 was found to be reminiscent of the rebuilding of 1853–55. It was typical of the style of the later ships of the brewing Civil War era. The original trailboard carvings by William Rush have long since disappeared. The trails now aboard, however, are already well over a century old, as is the billet head, both apparently made during or prior to 1855. The original figurehead is said to have been destroyed in the battle with *L'Insurgent* (9 February 1799).

In comparison with the trailboards on *Constitution* in Boston and those of the *Hartford* in the Mariners Museum, Newport News, it is apparent that the carvings on the *Constellation* are possibly the finest examples of such carvings in this country (Figure 12).

According to Franklin D. Roosevelt, the present trailboards were removed during the Civil War and replaced with "Wartime trails." [81] It was at least 15 years until they found their way back to the ship. During her service as a training ship through the 1870s, she had only a white painted stripe to serve as trails.

After many trials and experimental projections with the lines of the head rails and after consulting dozens of old contemporary prints and models at the Naval Academy, CRC finally settled upon what appeared to be a proper curve or "bag" of this distinctive feature in a ship of 1797. It was evident that the catheads, which play an important part in the location of these rails, were too far aft and their entire weight solely supported by a knee on the underside. Any pleasing curve which could be imparted to the eking of the seat rail came hard by the bridle ports beneath the catheads thereby rendering these openings ineffectual. The catheads were relocated above the forward edge of the bridle ports. It was also found advantageous to raise the catheads to the level of the top of plank sheer, which now provides positive support for the anchor bridling, the inboard ends being bolted through the spar deck to the beam at station 2 all in accordance with contemporary draughts and models. Now we were free to work the seat rail into the supporting knee curving forward and away from beneath the cathead. The actual "bag" of the head rails must first be based on the

rake and curve of the upper cheek of the trails. Each must complement the other in order to affect an eye appealing unit. This suggests that the shape of the rails are somewhat limited by the existing structure. This also suggests, however, that a diligent application of the one to the other must result in the shape we are looking for in the first place.

It was after considerable trial and error that the first sketches were finally transferred to an actual scale model. This consisted of a hair rail and a seat rail. Subject to critical examination, a midrail was added in order to gain further stiffening for the structure. This contributed to the esthetic beauty of the head but was not strictly in accord wih most of the old plans and so was soon deleted.

Finally, the preliminary sketches were set down on a new construction plan (No. C–400–1) along with offsets of the rails in order to loft the complex curves in a building fixture and then transfer the entire erection to the bows of the ship. On the new Outboard Profile (1960) the ten small head knees, are deleted and replaced by four much larger 8-inch white oak members, moulded 12 inches in depth.

The lacing pieces, plainly enough were in poor condition and obviously required replacement. The lacing cap, or tie piece, was in a short length, having been cut down. It was of good solid clear white oak and CRC hesitated before removing it but there was no alternative, as it must be long enough to carry out the function for which it was intended; that function being to secure the upper edges of the lacing pieces and the billet to the stem. The tailboards were carefully removed and laid out on the gun deck. Here they were photographed and inspected for deterioration. Aside from the loss of two small pieces of the trail cheek moulding, the carvings were found to be generally sound.

The gammoning irons of a later period were found to be bolted through the remaining existing lacing pieces. These were removed in the summer of 1964 in preparation for the restoration to the earlier rope gammonings.

Timber head bitts were nowhere in evidence on the spar deck. They are shown now on the plan of the spar deck and the Inboard Works (Plan No. C–100–1; Figure 3) as well as on the Outboard Profile (C–200–3). The timber heads are also shown on the sheer plan, at frames X, Y, Z and "a" (Plan No. C–100–4; Figure 10).

Knightheads and hawse pieces found on the ship, remain unchanged on the plans. *The Capps Report indicates replacement of the knightheads in 1853. This renewal was strikingly evident in comparison with the adjacent hawse pieces on the ship.* The hawse pieces angle back along the bows, forming a beakhead bulkhead, which is graphically illustrated on the plan of the spar deck as well as on the Lines Plan, in the sheers and half breadths. It was then painstakingly built up on a one-quarter-inch scale model before the actual reconstruction was begun.

FIGURE 12.—Head rails and cutwater of *Constellation:* top, July 1953; bottom, present.

Rigging channels were rebuilt and the chain plates are still substantially sound after several minor repairs. The rest of the iron work remains intact and is typical of the early period (pre-1853). It should be noted on later ships that the "chains" actually became iron or steel straps spreading the lower shrouds on the channels. A good example of this later "chain plate" is to be found on the restored *Constitution*.

Upon removal of the chain plates on the starboard side, it was found that wooden bushings had been inserted in the through-bolt holes *in the earlier frames* to take up the slack caused by elongation of those holes. One such bushing was removed from the aftermost chain of the fore mast, leading to the topgallant backstay. It is now preserved in the ship's archives. A chesstree timber from the main course tack, as reconstructed, was bolted to the hull at frame E.

The iron mooring staples on each side, removed during the replanking, are now reinstalled. In the report of Commander E. Delavey, 29 November 1926,[82] he points out that the forward staple on the port side was removed and replaced after repairs. In the process of heating one of the bolts, the retaining nut was dropped between the frames while red hot, showering sparks and causing a fire on the berth and orlop decks. The blackened timber is still in evidence though structurally sound.

Gun deck planking was found to have been sheathed with 4 x 1¾ inch pine. In July of 1964, the sheathing was removed laying bare the deck planking, 4 x 7 inch oak king plank on centerline and tapering to 3½ x 7 inch pine at the sides. The three waterway strakes are 6½ x 9 inches; the waterway log, 12 x 15 inches. It was at once noted that the outline of an earlier and somewhat larger capstan was inscribed in the deck plank in way of the present gear. It is just such evidence for which the researcher must be constantly alert.

The orlop deck fore and aft required practically no structural rebuilding. The knees and fastenings were found to be solid and tight. A small percentage of ceiling plank was in need of replacement on the sides in the main hold. Several deck beam ends were deficient under the berth and deck amidships. Repairs are under way.

Hatch beams and carlings of great age are sound and tough. The evident difference in longevity of timber is apparent, even to the unpracticed eye, when compared with that of the later deck coamings and knees in the upper 'tweens. This is not to say that all 'tween deck coamings were relaced with newer structural elements in 1853 as it seems abundantly apparent that wherever possible, the original beams and girders were reinstalled.

The lower orlop breast hook, as distinguished from the deck hooks, is one of the finest examples of original live oak timber yet exposed. This huge, naturally curved timber, comes down to us almost certainly from the shipyard of David Stodder. It, as well as the adjacent thrust knees, is one of the highlights of a tour through the ship. Although partially split at the throat due to the tension of the curved bow structure, the breast hook is still in one piece, functional, and intact.

The after orlop deck is composed of the following store rooms, arranged on each side of the cockpit: a sail locker, marines storeroom, captain's stores, two bread rooms, hospital stores, masters stores, midshipmen stores, officer stores and pursers stores. According to the notes of Thomas Truxtun, one steward's berth occupied the forward area athwart the centerline outside the sail locker in the glory hole.

Below the orlop deck are two magazines for the storage of ammunition, enclosed on all sides and illuminated by lamp boxes. Forward of the magazines is the spirit room and aft, the lazarette.

In the after hold at frame 26, the mizzen step of solid bronze and octagonal in shape is mounted upon the keelson, just abaft the magazine bulkhead. About 120 tons of pig iron ballast or kentledge is strung along the bilges from the spirit room, approximately frame 17 and forward, through the main hold and into the fore hold up to the foremast step at frame R. In areas where the bilge water has reached this ballast (some of which is apparently as old as the ship), it had deteriorated to a state of iron oxide. The scale, in some cases three-eighths inches thick, was easily broken off with the bare fingers.

In March of 1963, CRC was finally in a position to shift a large portion of the amidship ballast from the ship's bottom in order to flush and clean the main lower hold and bilges (Figure 13).

The ballast now began to move, lifted piece by piece from its resting place in the bottom to the platform which was left available on the sides at the turn of the bilges. Each pig iron bar, varying in weight from 150 to 350 pounds was hove up in its turn finally laying bare the keelson, floors, bottom planking, ceiling stringers, limber strakes and boxing upon which the bars had been stacked so many years before.

FIGURE 13.—Fore hold of *Constellation* showing iron ballast. (Courtesy of the *Baltimore Sunpapers*.)

Now indeed was an opportunity to sound out these timbers with the ever present inspection pick. A check of each structural component soon revealed that the bottom, in general terms was sound and tight. The outer planking, a particular source of concern when tested (from the inside, of course) appeared to be sound enough. This was a reassuring examination, preliminary to the final test on the outer surface.

Sadly enough, all the news was not good. Several areas of "iron sickness" were found involving almost 30 percent of the stringers under the ballast bars. This led to a substantial increase in the restoration estimate of material and labor. Also noted was the deteriorated condition of the three sea cock bolsters. The valves themselves of cast bronze appeared to be in fine condition except for the usual patina which formed on the surfaces, but it was almost certain that they would have to be dismounted in order to secure the watertight integrity of the penetrations.

During the summer of 1964, while in drydock, the ballast was scaled and painted with white lead. Next, each bar was replaced in racks out of reach of the bilge water. The flood cocks on *Constellation* are located strategically adjacent to the magazines in the fore and after holds, and in the waist section, or main hold.

The keelson moulds 34 inches from the throat line to top of cap and sides 17 inches. It is a product of the rebuilding of 1853–55 as is also the fore and aft deadwood timbers, the stern post, apron of the stem (stem liner) and about 15 feet of the stem itself. CRC's careful examination of the stem reveals that it tapers from an 18-inch breadth at the fore foot, to 17 inches as it progresses upwards from the 12-foot waterline. The keel is 18 inches broad and 30 inches moulded (mean depth). This was recorded, as determined at the Boston Navy Yard, shown on their Docking Plan.[83] They are the same as the dimensions given by David Stodder in his letter dated 30 April 1795. These dimensions were again soon to be determined by the restoration committee during the drydocking of 28 May 1964 (see p. 139). Critical dimensions in way of the keel assembly are: rabbet of keel, 4 inches; deadwood, 4 inches; floor timber, 16 inches; throat to under side of berth deck beam, 13 feet 2½ inches (depth of hold).

As to the keel section, no one knew what the garboard scantlings consisted of, nor was there any more than speculative information as to the manner of fastening together of the floor timbers, the deadwood, and the keel. The resulting plan of the midship section (Figure 14) is evolved from untold numbers of sketches, trial and error calculations, physical measurements on the ship and comparisons with plans of contemporary ships, circa 1795–1860. Floor timbers throughout, were found to be sound and solid in the ship's bottom.

Two anchors arrived in Baltimore with the ship. They are typical of the early oak stock bowers. One is unmarked and listed as "old" in the delivery inventory. The other is stamped 8100 lbs. 1858. The plans of 1888 show typical kedge anchors of the period catted up on billboards alongside the spar deck. On the new plans of 1960, these have been replaced with the typical bower anchors, at this moment on the beach alongside the ship.

It is of interest to note the various methods of determining anchor sizes in the mid-19th century. From John Lenthall's "Equipment List: Articles Under the Cognizance of the Bureau of Equipment and Recruiting," [84] we note on p. 33 the formula, "multiply the square of her extreme breadth by the number assigned to her rate . . . in the . . . table" (2.8 for a Sloop of War, 2nd or 3rd rate). "The product will express the number of pounds exclusive of stock, but inclusive of bending shackle." Thus, $422 \times 2.8 = 4939$ pounds. If the constant, 3.0 (*for frigates of the 2nd rate, razeed*) is applied, the resultant weight of each bower anchor will be *5292* pounds. The Boston Navy Yard Capacity Plan dated May 1859 lists the weight as 5615 pounds,[85] a negligible difference. To quote Lenthall, "This rule will give the intended weights, but . . . discretion will be exercised. . . ." [86]

In summary we note: the anchors of a Sloop of War are too small by 661 pounds; the plan of 1859 shows anchors of a *razeed frigate,* a description which surely fit *Constellation* after the 1853 alteration; and the weight differential is insignificant at 323 pounds. Sketches and eventually new drawings were made depicting the anchors.[87] The iron bound oak stocks were in poor condition, requiring much repair. All dimensions for the new drawings were taken directly from the work.

DRYDOCKING.—The underwater body: If CRC could tabulate all of its anxieties concerning the structural integrity of the ship (as a matter of fact the very immediate safety of *Constellation*), there is little doubt that from 1959 until the spring of 1964, drydocking would head the list. It must be remembered that the committee had never seen the underwater body, the garboards, the keel, the lower stem or the stern post. The day finally arrived on 28 May 1964.[88] As the noon whistle blew at the shipyard in Baltimore *Constellation* cleared the water.

As the inspection team stepped out on the dock, the first detail to be noted was the copper sheath covering the entire underwater surface from the 20 foot waterline to and including the keel. Here it had been hoped to find a relatively narrow belt of copper. An estimate of approximately $4000 was drawn to remove this sheath in order to get at the planking and caulking. The work progressed all through the night and by the end of the second day, the wood hull was laid bare and sand-washed.

In the area of research the breadth of the keel had long confounded everyone. The offsets of 1853 give this dimension as 17 inches which is of course, contrary to the 18-inch dimension described by David Stodder, the builder. The Restoration Committee, up to this point, leaned heavily upon the measurements taken at the Boston Navy Yard in 1946 to substantiate the claim that the original keel still existed, in reference to its dimensions.[89] CRC therefore immediately set about taking off dimensions at various points along the keel. It was found that for the greatest length, every dimension in breadth *exceeded* 17 inches, generally varying from $17\frac{1}{2}$ inches to a full 18 inches.

On 17 June 1964, one loose copper bolt dated W 1812 was withdrawn from the keel near the stern post. This was surmised to be part of Captain Tingey's repair at the Washington Navy Yard during that year. The bearing surface (length) of the bolt driven from side to side of the keel is 18 inches. This was not the first dated bolt to be found in the hull. On 19 May 1960, there was withddrawn from frame 21, plank 21, starboard side, a 13-inch long bolt dated "1797." A final word on the copper hull fastening bolts. Figure 15*e* is an enlargement of the date stamp, 1797, on a copper fastening bolt removed from the hull during the 1960 drydocking of the *Constellation*. Immediately following the discovery of this bolt, as well as the one stamped "W 1812," affidavits were drawn up and signed by the shipyard workmen.

FIGURE 15.—Markings on copper bolts from contemporary ships: a, Gosport Navy Yard from *Constellation;* b, Washington Navy Yard from *Constellation;* c, from *New Hampshire;* d, from *Constitution;* e, from *Constellation.*

The letter (Figure 16) from the Kennecott Refining Corp. is a report of a professional comparison analysis of the bolts in order to determine the difference between the copper of 1797 used in the ship and later bolts of 1853. It will be seen that the comparison reveals a distinct increase in antimony and arsenic as we compare the earlier to the later fastenings. As the chemists state, indications are, at the least, "that they came from two different sources."

Note also that no cobalt is found in the bolts dated 1797, 1812, and one additional bolt dated 1808. Also the gold content of the 1853 bolt is more than double that in the fastenings of 1797 or 1812 and more than three times the content in the bolt of 1808. A substantial difference is also indicated in the silver content of the four bolts.

The theory has been advanced that some of the "old" fastenings were re-used for nostalgic reasons or perhaps to imbed in an "administratively built" ship some proof that it is in fact the "old" ship. This theory is of little practical value when removed from the "library mechanic" to the cold reality of a construction plant foreman. There are several penalties for reusing soft copper bolts, spikes, or rivets previously cold formed or peined on opposite ends. When removed the bar is generally malformed and the ends now upset must be cut off, reducing the length by about 2 inches. Let us consider where to use these fastenings of varied lengths, now too short to be installed in a similar location on a "new" construction—and they will be 2 inches shorter when again tightened in the new structure! To compound the problem, if the older fastening is to appear normal, it must be of the same length and diameter as the new bolts surrounding it. It is evident that certain production penalties must occur in the practice of this theory.

The most surprising of all discoveries was the keel to stem connection. This certainly is not the arrangement of timbers as shown by John Lenthall in 1853. Also it did not appear to be a repair (see Figure 17). The lowest extremity of the stem is located 40 inches above the baseline and ten inches above the lower rabbet. The hooked scarph joint shown on Lenthall's plan of May 1853 was not in evidence and the stem planed off in a horizontal line at the foot is bolted directly to the keel and further secured laterally by bronze fish plates.

The keel, built up in two sections, is also secured by a double set of bronze retainers or fish plates. These are beautifully inletted into the timbers on both sides at the stem and at the post.

The keel shoe does not meet the forefoot in the manner shown by Lenthall in 1853 and reproduced on CRC's own plans in 1959–60. The pieces are butted directly to each other fore and aft and to the stem shoe. As Lenthall depicts the arrangement, the stem shoe overlaps its counterpart on the underside of the keel.

These observations are significant in themselves. The inspection team could find nowhere in its files a record of repairs which could relate itself to this peculiar arrangement. In 1853 a new piece of stem 15 feet, 10 inches long was installed.[90] This would be about 13 feet short of reaching the forefoot. Similarly in 1829, 15 feet of stem was replaced, apparently the same piece. Even if a repair was reported in the area of the forefoot, how could it have changed the profile of the keel in this manner? The keel itself rises up to meet the stem, well above the straight rabbet.

Kennecott Refining Corporation

SUBSIDIARY OF KENNECOTT COPPER CORPORATION

Post Office Box 3407

Baltimore, Maryland 21226

March 18, 1969

Constellation Restoration Committee
Pier 4, Pratt Street
Baltimore, Maryland 21202

Gentlemen:

      Listed below are the impurity contents of the copper pins
you recently submitted to our analytical laboratory. We understand
these pins were removed from the structural members of the U.S.
FRIGATE CONSTELLATION.'

	Pin Marked 1797	Pin Marked 1812-USNYW	Pin Marked 1808 (large dia.)	Pin Marked 1853-55GNY
Tin (per cent)	.00029	.0035	.0094	.00027
Lead (per cent)	.068	.093	.17	.26
Bismuth (per cent)	.0037	.085	.0048	.0080
Nickel (per cent)	.040	.12	.027	.075
Antimony (per cent)	.0058	.013	.0090	.11
Arsenic (per cent)	.019	.11	.036	.17
Iron (per cent)	.00072	.00094	.00068	.00075
Tellurium (per cent)	.00055	.0017	.00038	.00070
Selenium (per cent)	.020	.010	<.010	.013
Cobalt (per cent)	N.D.*	N.D.	N.D.	trace
Gold (oz/T**)	.205	.230	.085	.480
Silver (oz/T)	8.38	9.09	9.10	12.49

* None detected
** Troy ounces per avoirdupois ton

-2-

      I understand you are particularly interested in whether
the 1797 pin and the GNY pin came from the same source. A comparison of the respective lead, antimony, and arsenic contents of these
two pins indicates that they came from two different sources.

      Most of the impurities were analyzed spectrographically
by Mr. Albert A. DiLeonardi, Chief Chemist. Gold and silver were
analyzed using fire assay techniques by Mr. Leo E. O'Hara, Laboratory
Technician.

Very truly yours,

N. A. Wood.

W. A. Wood
Quality Control Director

WAW:bes

cc: A. A. DiLeonardi
     L. E. O'Hara
     W. P. Visick
     C. A. Zeldin

FIGURE 16.—Letter from W. A. Wood, Quality Control Director, Kennecott Refining Corporation
to *Constellation* Restoration Committee, 18 March 1969.

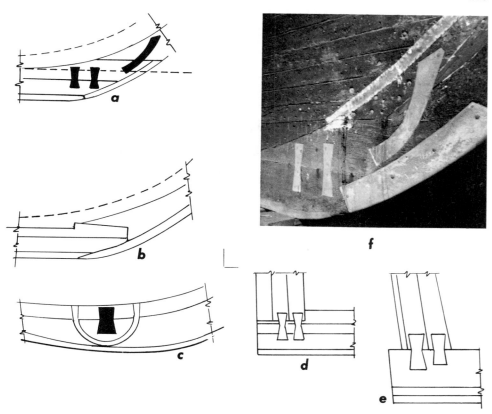

FIGURE 17.—Stem to keel connection of *Constellation:* a, f, arrangement of timbers and fish plates noted upon drydocking, 1964; b, John Lenthall's conception (C & R Plan, No. 28–3–5) of arrangement of timbers; c, similar areas on H.M.S. *Victory* showing similar use of bronze fish plates; d–e, fish plates in way of keel and stern posts of *Constellation* and H.M.S. *Victory,* respectively.

There seemed to be no alternative but to conclude that Lenthall drew his plan before he saw the keel and his projected scarph still remains on the drawing to this day; and the Restoration Committee is quite familiar with the Delano statement that the "underwater body of Constellation does not match drawing of Humphrey plan *or the sketched drawings 1852*" [91] (italics mine).

In the following letter from the War Office to David Stodder, reference is made to his "model of a scarph." While we must hesitate to make an unsupported claim, it is worthwhile noting that the stem to keel connection surveyed during the drydocking in 1964 did not agree with the plan of John Lenthall, nor indeed does it bear a similarity to any of the Admiralty models or plans in our library of contemporary American ships. The only ship structure known to us at this writing bearing a resemblance to this element of the keel assembly is to be found on H.M.S. *Victory* which

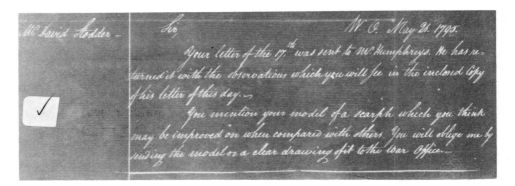

FIGURE 18.—Letter from War Office to David Stodder, 21 May 1795
(National Archives, Washington, D.C., Record Group 45).

exhibits remarkably similar fish plates in way of the forefoot, as well as the stern post. *Victory,* of course, was first built in *1765.* Our correspondence with the former constructor of many years at H. M. Dockyard, Portsmouth, indicates the fish plates to date from *Victory's* earliest construction. The fish plates at the stem, keel, and post connections of *Constellation* are almost identical to those found on H.M.S. *Victory.* It is suggested that this peculiar construction of *Constellation's* keel is related to the "model of a scarph" referenced by David Stodder, from the War Office.[92]

Judging by the content of the letter dated 21 May 1795, we can safely assume that Stodder was rather concerned about methods of scarphing certain timbers. Since his letter of 30 April [93] already indicated that the keel and floors were assembled, we might now imply that he had in mind the stem-to-keel connections. This information would certainly complement our observations on the already noted "fish plates" found on *Constellation* (1797) and *Victory* (1765).

Stodder was concerned enough to have constructed a model illustrating his "new ideas." Of course, we cannot as this writing, claim with certainty that there is a primary connection between the letter and the peculiarities of the stem-keel and post-keel structures, but is such a possibility inconceivable?

Our function is to present the material as it was found. Various interpretations may be assigned to this document but until a better time we shall be content to let the reader ponder this one final item: The *Constellation* Committee has within its files many documents concerning the ship. It is not physically possible within these pages to catalog those papers. That project must one day be undertaken for there is still more to tell.

TABLE 1.—*Principal Dimensions of U.S. Frigate* Constellation

	Feet	Inches
Length between perpendiculars	176	0
Beam moulded outside of frame	41	0
Hold to gun deck	21	4½

The base line is the lower edge of the rabbet of the keel.

The forward perpendicular is at the intersection of the fore side of the rabbet of the stem with a waterline 17 feet above the lower edge of the rabbet of the keel.

The after perpendicular is at the intersection of the aft side of the rabbet of the stern post with a water line 17 feet above the lower edge of the rabbet of the keel.

	Feet	Inches
Timber and room	2	8
Distance of fictitious timber b from fore perpendicular	1	1
Distance from frame b to amidships	74	8
Distance from amidships to frame 36	96	0
Distance of fictitious frame 36 from after perpendicular	4	3
Length between perpendiculars	176	0
Distance of forward square frame R from forward perpendicular	27	9
Distance of after square frame 28 from after perpendicular	25	7

Height at amidships above lower edge of rabbet of keel

	Feet	Inches
Rabbet of keel	0	4
Deadwood	0	4
Throat of floor timber	1	4
Hold to underside of berth deck beam	13	2½
Berth deck beam moulded	1	0½
Berth deck plank	0	3½
Height from berth deck plank to underside of gun deck beam	5	9
Gun deck beam moulded	1	1
Gun deck plank	0	4½
Height of top of gun deck plank amidships	23	9
Deduct the spring of the beam		5
Height of the top of gun deck plank at the side	23	4
Height under the spar deck beam	6	0
Spar deck beam moulded	0	8
Spar deck plank	0	3½
Plank sheer above the deck	0	9½
Height of top of plank sheer above lower edge of rabbet of keel (amidships)	31	1
Height of the top of gun deck plank at the side	23	4
Port sill above the deck	2	0
Height of lower port sill above lower edge of rabbet of keel	25	4
Port in height	3	0
Height of upper port sill above lower edge of rabbet of keel	28	4

NOTES

[1] *Transactions of the Society of Naval Architects and Marine Engineers* (1914), vol. 22, 139–155. Presented to the Society in New York, 10 December 1914.

[2] Ibid., p. 153.

[3] General Services Administration National Archives and Record Services (Franklin D. Roosevelt Library, Hyde Park, New York).

[4] THEODORE ROOSEVELT, *The Naval War of 1812,* 1st ed. (New York: G. P. Putnam's Sons, 1882).

[5] *American State Papers, Documents Legislative and Executive of Congress of the United States, from the First Session of the First to the Second Session of the 18th Congress inclusive, commencing March 3, 1789 and ending March 5, 1825* (Washington, 1834), vol. 1: Naval Affairs. *Constellation* dimensions given on 20 January 1794.

[6] Record Group 19: Records of the Bureau of Ships (National Archives, Washington, D.C.).

[7] Lenthall Documents Collection (Franklin Institute, Philadelphia, Pennsylvania).

[8] *Constellation* Docking Plan, No. IX–20–50700–661826 dated 30 September 1946 (Boston Navy Yard, Massachusetts). See also National Archives Record Group 19 (footnote 6).

[9] Draught of 36-Gun Frigate (Frigates *Congress* and *Constellation,* 36 Guns), signed by William Doughty, 1794 (United States Naval Academy Museum, United States Naval Academy, Annapolis, Maryland).

[10] Lenthall Documents Collection (footnote 7).

[11] National Archives Record Group 19 (footnote 6).

[12] Journal of Captain Thomas Truxtun (Franklin Institute, Philadelphia, Pennsylvania).

[13] THOMAS NICHOLS, "Observations on the Use of Iron Knees," *Papers for the Society for the Improvement of Naval Architecture* (London, 1795), article XXXV, p. 37. See also M. THOMAS, "Seppings on Ship-Building," *The Analetic Magazine* (Philadelphia, 1815), vol. 6, p. 456. "It is a well known fact, that the Insurgent, taken from the French by Commodore Truxtun in 1799, sixteen years ago was built with iron knees."

[14] Lenthall Documents Collection (footnote 7).

[15] General Services Administration National Archives and Record Services (footnote 3).

[16] Inboard Works and Deck Plans (Final Draught), No. C–100–1 by L. D. Polland, 26 June 1959, in LEON D. POLLAND, *The Frigate "Constellation": An Outline of the Present Restoration,* 2nd ed. (Society of Naval Architects and Marine Engineers, 1968). Also in files of the *Constellation* Restoration Committee of Baltimore.

[17] Lenthall Documents Collection (footnote 7).

[18] National Archives Record Group 19 (footnote 6).

[19] *Naval Documents Relating to the Barbary Wars* (Washington, D.C.: United States Government Printing Office, 1939), vol. 1, p. 69.

[20] Transcribed statement of Captain Tingey, Superintendent, Washington Navy Yard. *Constellation* file 1231–A: "Major Battle Damage, Repairs and Reconstruction to U.S. Ship Constellation, 1797–1855" by Admiral W. L. Capps, at direction of Truman H. Newberry, Assistant Secretary of Navy (Library of Naval War College, U.S. Naval Training Station, Newport Rhode Island).

[21] *Constellation* file (Library of Naval War College, U.S. Naval Training Station, Newport, Rhode Island). Transcribed letter.

[22] Record Group 45: Naval Records Collection of the Office of Naval Records and Library (National Archives, Washington, D.C.).

[23] File IX–21–M7–2(N) 31 (Boston Navy Yard, Massachusetts).

[24] "Report on Work Completed at the Philadelphia Navy Yard, 30 October to 26 November 1926" by Commander E. DeLavey dated 29 November 1926. National Archives Record Group 45 (footnote 22).

[25] Pickering File (Historical Society of Pennsylvania, Philadelphia, Pennsylvania).

[26] National Archives Record Group 19 (footnote 6). Plan of Transverse Sections, C&R Plan 107–13–4B dated February 1853.

[27] National Archives Record Group 45 (footnote 22). Transcribed sheet from Delano notebook.

[28] Record Group 71: Records of Bureau of Yards and Docks, Navy Yard, Gosport Log Book 1851–1855 (National Archives, Washington, D.C. Letters from Commandant, Gosport Navy Yard January–June 1853; November 1853–May 1854.

[29] Record Group 45: Naval Records Collection of the Office of Naval Records and Library, Entry 374: The War Department Records of the Federal Government, 1790–1831 (National Archives, Washington, D.C.). Letters sent concerning Naval matters, October 1790–June 1798.

[30] Ibid., Letter from Pickering to Stodder, 18 May 1795. "You are the owner of a Navy Yard and also a master builder . . ."

[31] EUGENE FERGUSON, *Truxtun of the Constellation* (Baltimore: Johns Hopkins Press, 1956), chapter 25. Outlines the problems of procuring timber from Georgia.

[32] National Archives Record Group 45 (footnote 29). John Morgans appointment as constructor at Norfolk, 8 August 1794.

[33] FERGUSON, op. cit.

[34] ROOSEVELT, op. cit. (footnote 4), p. 72.

[35] (New York, Lea and Blanchard, 1839), vol. 2, p. 197.

[36] POLLAND, op. cit. (footnote 16), p. 17, 19.

[37] Transcribed statement of Captain Tingey (footnote 20).

[38] Ibid.

[39] "Our First Frigates," loc. cit. (footnote 1).

[40] File of the *Constellation* Restoration Committee of Balimore.

[41] *U.S.F. Constitution* (booklet) (Washington, D.C.: United States Government Printing Office, 1932).

[42] Transcribed statement of Captain Tingey (footnote 20).

[43] National Archives Record Group 45 (footnote 20). Plan (fragment) of Constellation, Mizzen Mast Survey 1840 (1829). Note initials F.D.R. on lower right margin.

[44] Transcribed statement of Samuel Humphreys on enlarging and rounding the stern in 1829. In *Constellation* file (Library of Naval War College, U.S. Naval Training Station, Newport, Rhode Island). "Report listed as other than battle damage and the specifications for repairs are from Ware and Tare at sea." "Repair 1828–1829. Released from Gosport Navy Yard 1829 (Specifications) . . . To newly fasion [sic] the underbody of the stern . . . and to round the counter to a full body curve. . . ."

[45] POLLAND, op cit. (footnote 16), p. 36. See also Transcribed statement of Captain Tingey (footnote 20).

[46] *Barbary Wars—Personnel and Ships Data 1801–1807*. Published under direction of the Honorable James V. Forrestal, Secretary of the Navy (Washington, D.C.: United States Government Printing Office, 1945), p. 71. Includes National Archives ships plan 41–9–1L.

[47] The Henry Huddleston Rogers Ship Model Collection (United States Naval Academy Museum, Annapolis, Maryland).

[48] Inboard Works and Deck Plans (footnote 16).

[49] Draught of 36-Gun Frigate (footnote 9).

[50] Tingey and Charles Stewart Papers (Library of Congress, Washington, D.C.).

[51] Journal of Captain Thomas Truxtun (footnote 12).

[52] Transcribed statement of Captain Tingey (footnote 20).

[53] Inboard Works and Deck Plans (footnote 16).

[54] POLLAND, op. cit. (footnote 16), p. 36. Capps Report, "Major Repairing—1828".

[55] Franklin Institute, Philadelphia, Pennsylvania.

[56] National Archives Record Group 19 (footnote 6).

[57] National Archives Record Group 45 (footnote 22).

[58] Ibid. (footnote 20), Dimensions and offsets of 44- and 36-gun frigates, by Joshua Humphreys, 30 July 1795.

[59] National Archives Record Group 19 (footnote 6).

[60] National Archieves Record Group 71 (footnote 28).

[61] POLLAND, op. cit. (footnote 16), p. 40.

[62] Ibid.

[63] Inboard Works and Deck Plans (footnote 16).

[64] National Archives Record Group 19 (footnote 6).

[65] Ibid. (footnote 5), "Constellation—1853· Dimensions of the Spar deck Sloop of War Constellation taken from the Mould loft floor."

[66] POLLAND, op. cit. (footnote 16), Lines Plan, No. C–100–4 by L. D. Polland, 27 May 1961.

[67] LOUIS GOTTSCHALK, *The Use of Personal Documents in History, Anthropology, and Sociology* (New York: Social Science Research Council, 1924), p. 36. "For each particular of a document the process of establishing credibility should be separately undertaken."

[68] National Archives Record Group (footnote 6).

[69] Draught of 36-Gun Frigate (footnote 9).

[70] National Archives Record Group 19 (footnote 6), "Constellation—1853: Dimensions of the Spar deck Sloop of War Constellation taken from the Mould loft floor."

[71] Inboard Works and Deck Plans (footnote 16).

[72] Ibid. See also Midship Section Plan, No. C–100–3 by L. D. Polland, 10 September 1959 and Lines Plan, No. C–1004 by L. D. Polland, 27 May 1961.

[73] Inboard Works and Deck Plans (footnote 16).

[74] Offsets signed by Josiah Fox 20 October 1795 in Josiah Fox Papers (Peabody Marine Museum, Salem, Massachusetts). "Heels of facing timbers are to run two feet below upper edge of gun deck beams."

[75] Lenthall Documents Collection (footnote 7).

[76] National Archives Record Group 45 (footnote 22), Letter from Lenthall to Skinner, 18 December 1851.

[77] Plan of Dimensions and Offsets Plan, No. C–100–5 by L. D. Polland, 20 April 1961, in files of the *Constellation* Restoration Committee of Baltimore.

[78] *Constellation* Docking Plan (footnote 8).

[79] *Constellation* Docking Plan, No. IX–20–50700–85990, 22 October 1946. (Boston Navy Yard, Massachusetts).

[80] "Report on Work Completed" (footnote 24).

[81] FRANKLIN D. ROOSEVELT, "Constellation Trailboards" (Mrs. Franklin D. Roosevelt Library, Hyde Park, New York).

[82] "Report of Work Completed" (footnote 24).

[83] *Constellation* Docking Plan (footnote 79).

[84] File of the *Constellation* Restoration Committee of Baltimore.

[85] National Archives Record Group 19 (footnote 6).

[86] [John Lenthall's "Equipment List"] (footnote 84), p. 33.

[87] *Constellation* Anchors Plan, No. C–300–2 by L. D. Polland, 31 August 1959, in file of *Constellation* Restoration Committee of Baltimore.

[88] *Constellation* was drydocked at Maryland Shipbuilding & Drydock Company, Baltimore, Maryland.

[89] *Constellation* Docking Plan (footnote 79).

[90] Transcribed statement of Captain Tingey (footnote 20).

[91] National Archives Record Group 45 (footnote 22).

[92] Record Group 45 (footnote 29).

[93] Pickering File (footnote 25).

Index

DATE DUE

GAYLORD			PRINTED IN U.S.A.